CANADA'S CENTURY

by

D. M. LeBOURDAIS

THE METHUEN COMPANY OF CANADA
LIMITED
TORONTO   -:-   LONDON

...ction of Peace River Canyon

First Published, 1951

971
3943

PRINTED AND BOUND IN CANADA
by
T. H. Best Printing Co., Limited, Toronto

To Louis
Who loved the North

Preface

During many years of writing about Canada, I have been hampered by the lack of books describing the country as a whole. Aside from necessarily inadequate school geographies, the physical makeup of Canada has been largely ignored by writers for the general public. If, for example, one wishes a book for a stranger that will tell him the sort of country Canada is, and the sort of livelihood it might provide, one will search in vain. There is Professor Griffith Taylor's excellent *Canada*, of course, although somewhat too technical for the average reader.

Books there are on some of the Provinces, notably Nova Scotia and Newfoundland, with a few more on particular sections of the country, such as the parts of Ontario and Quebec frequented by tourists, and the North; but they fail to give a comprehensive picture of Canada.

Likewise, a great many articles have been written about various parts of the country; but, again, there is no over-all picture. The splendid accounts of explorations written by members of the Geological Survey of Canada during more than a century provide what comes nearest to a complete Canadian mosaic, but these are seen by few other than specialists. I should like, however, to express my admiration for the work of these men, among whom may be found many really great Canadians. To them and to their records I am indebted for more than this book shows. I wish also, in this regard, to acknowledge my debt to my friend Vilhjalmur Stefansson, whose influence may more easily be discerned.

As will be seen, I have concentrated chiefly on the less-known parts of Canada, which, in my opinion, are destined, because of their natural wealth, to become the determining factor in its future. I have also attempted to show that the once-considered wasteland barriers in reality tie the country together.

In securing and verifying my material, I have made use of several Departments of the Federal Government, as well as some Provincial Departments; and I have received information and advice from many persons whose special knowledge has been of value to me. To name any of these would be invidious, but each will, I hope, accept my thanks as here expressed.

The Frontispiece, from a photograph by Richard Harrington, is published with the kind permission of the Hudson's Bay Company's Magazine, *The Beaver*; and photographs opposite pages 20, 21, and 31, also by Richard Harrington, are reproduced with his permission. Photographs opposite pages 30, 63, 79, and 150 are by the National Film Board; those opposite pages 46, 47, and 62, were supplied by the Aluminum Company of Canada Limited; the Shawinigan Water and Power Company; and Spruce Falls Power and Paper Company Limited, respectively. The photograph opposite page 78 was contributed by the Manitoba Bureau of Travel and Publicity; and those opposite pages 126, 127, 142, 143, and 182, by the Canadian National Railways.

The maps and end-papers were drawn by F. P. Lloyd, whom I wish to thank for an appreciative understanding of my need.

Finally, my thanks to Dr. A. Y. Jackson and to Mr. W. J. Bennett, President of Eldorado Mining and Refining (1944) Limited, for permission to reproduce on the jacket Dr. Jackson's splendid painting of Port Radium, Great Bear Lake, which adds distinction to the book.

D. M. LeBourdais.

Toronto, February 15, 1951.

Contents

Illustrations

1

Introduction

CANADA today stands at the threshold of what might easily prove to be a marvellous future. Nearly fifty years ago, in a burst of optimism, Sir Wilfrid Laurier declared that the twentieth century would be Canada's, but on the evidence then available it must be admitted that this and similar assertions of the time were derived from hope rather than factual information. Today, such an assertion might well be made on the strength of two factors alone: oil and iron ore. Even without these two important products, but taking into account her gold, silver, copper, nickel, and other minerals—including uranium,—so widely and generously distributed, in addition to timber and waterpower, Canada might have been assured of a very promising future. The presence, however, of oil and iron ore in such quantities as has been disclosed within the past two or three years, makes this a much greater possibility, and will also doubtless enhance Laurier's fame as a prophet.

Let us see what sort of a country Canada was at the time that Laurier's boast was made. Canada then, with but seven provinces, consisted chiefly of a narrow strip of territory strung along a single railway crossing the country not far from its southern border. This long, thin line connected small, isolated communities separated by considerable stretches of wilderness. The railway itself had been completed to the Pacific coast only 14 years earlier, and was still in many places a very primitive affair. Canada had then but 5,351,315 people (1901 census), 71 per cent of whom lived

1

in the Provinces of Ontario and Quebec, with only 12 per cent in the immense region between the head of the Great Lakes and the Pacific Ocean. The three Maritime Provinces had 893,953 people; Montreal had 267,730; Toronto had 208,040; and Ottawa was next in line with 59,928.

The iron ore of Ungava and Labrador was known to those few who read geological reports; but for all practical purposes it might as well have been in the moon. The extent of the Alberta coalfields was known, but these were then so remote from the main centres of population as to count for very little in the national economy. The only oilfields were in western Ontario, incapable of producing more than enough kerosene to fill Canadian lamps and stable-lanterns; and since the motor age had not yet arrived, practically no demand existed at all for that other petroleum product, gasoline, which has since become so important.

The placer fields of the Klondike supplied most of Canada's gold—the great lode mines of Ontario and Quebec were still below Time's horizon. Nickel, until recently considered a nuisance by those attempting to extract copper from the complex Sudbury ore, had not yet found its multitude of uses, and production in 1901 was valued at less than $10 million, while the copper produced was valued at less than $7 million. The total mineral production of Canada in 1901 amounted to only $66 million. Canada, now famed as one of the world's leading wheat producing countries, then produced about 55 million bushels a year, little of it grading No. 1, Northern. Canadian forests produced sawmill products valued at $117 million, and pulp and paper at $151 million. Canadian rapids and waterfalls then generated only 71,000 horsepower.

At the beginning of the century, the general view was that the immense region lying north of the settled zone was largely wasteland. Aside from the copper-nickel ore of Sudbury, which seemed somewhat in the nature of a sport, and a few small mineral occurrences near the western end of Lake Superior, nothing of value had yet been found in the Precambrian rocks of which this vast territory mainly consists.

Furthermore, this region of granitic rocks was covered by so sparse a soil that not much in the way of crops could be grown, even if the climate would permit; and nearly everyone was convinced that the climate was such that none but Indians and Eskimos would ever willingly live there.

It was also the general impression—which still largely prevails,—that Canada is so divided by barren stretches that the evolution of a unified, closely-knit community was forever impossible. One such barrier cut off the Maritime Provinces from central Canada; the region north of Lakes Huron and Superior effectively separated Old Ontario from the Prairies; the Rocky Mountains practically divorced British Columbia from the rest of the country; and the rock-bound North confined Canada in perpetuity to a narrow strip consisting of a few relatively small sections in which people could live in comparative comfort.

However, since half the century has now passed, we may fairly ask whether Canada's progress in that period was such as to justify the optimists, whatever the basis of their optimism. And, considering what has since been disclosed concerning Canada's possibilities, and what might have been accomplished had they been more fully appreciated earlier, it must be admitted that Canada, until quite recently, has not entirely justified these hopes. Although evidence has been piled on evidence, Canadians have been desperately slow to apprciate the value of the northern hinterland upon which their chief hope of greatness is now seen to depend. No country can be great in these days that does not have an ample supply of the metals essential to modern civilization which this region provides in such abundance. The basis of civilization is still the ability to provide food, clothing, and shelter, while allowing sufficient leisure for more intangible but no less essential requirements. Yet not till the arrival of the power-metal age has this been possible.

Not only did most Canadians fail to recognize the importance of this region, but many at times seemed to resent any suggestion that it might play a very vital part in their future. Out of this attitude has grown a "Little Canada" complex. It may be that, in the circumstances, estimates of Canada's ability to absorb people were, at one time, overly optimistic; but, of late, the pessimists have certainly been calling the tune. In 1949, one of these wrote that Canada could never hope to support more than 28 to 30 million people. This was no snap judgment, but a statement buttressed by seemingly well-reasoned arguments supporting the view that Canada could never be much more than a second-rate country. It is such thinking, by no means uncommon, which, in the past, has resulted in the failure of Canadians to measure up to the requirements of a great nation; and it is perhaps significant that the chief protagonist of a greater Canada should be the geographer, Dr. Griffith Taylor, a former Australian.

During an unwarranted (as measured by later events) period of optimism, Canadian railway promoters equipped the country with a greater per capita railway mileage than any country in the world. This was not the intention, of course, for at that time everyone expected great and immediate increases in population. Then, having built the railways, Canadians, by restricting immigration and neglecting the opening-up of new territory, made it almost impossible for any but the most favourably-situated ones to operate at a profit.

A case in point is the Grand Trunk Railway scheme, evolved in the expansive early years of the century, to build a transcontinental railway, largely with public money, from Moncton, N. B., to Prince Rupert, B. C., to provide the shortest route across the continent. The idea was basically sound; but, in most parts, the country through which it runs was left largely undeveloped, and consequently could provide little traffic; while Prince Rupert, which might by now have become an important seaport, was left out on the end of a limb. The short-sightedness of this is evident when it is realized that many problems that have plagued Canada for most of the past half-century might have been greatly lessened had this potentially-productive region been brought under use.

In 1922, the International Joint Commission recommended completion of the Great Lakes-St. Lawrence Waterway. The Commission, a continuing one, consists of three Canadians and three Americans, and their recommendation in this case was unanimous. Steady opposition has come from certain United States interests; but if opposition had not also come from Canadian sources, it is possible that the waterway might by now have been completed.

In 1929, after a series of unjustifiable delays, a railway reached Churchill, on Hudson Bay, and docks and a grain elevator were built there; but full advantage of the Hudson Bay rail and sea route has never been taken. This is due, not only to the persistent opposition of those interested in other routes, but also to the indifference of Canadians elsewhere who assume that because they may not derive a direct benefit from it the matter is of little concern to them.

Finally, no country that aspired to a position among the leading nations of the world would for so long have been content with a situation in which she was unable to amend her constitution without recourse to a legislature beyond her borders. Neither would such a country have been content to let her legal cases be settled in a final court of appeal presided over by judges belonging to another country. That almost half a century should have been required for such obvious reforms in itself indicates a serious lack of self-confidence.

Let us see, then, what might have been accomplished in

the first half of the twentieth century if Canadians had been the sort of people who might hope to outstrip the world before its end. A more northerly zone across Canada could have been opened up and consolidated with the regions farther south. This would have given the country badly-needed breadth, and would much sooner have made available the mineral wealth and hydroelectric power now being produced there. Development of this region could have been advanced by taking advantage of the shorter routes to world markets provided by Prince Rupert and Churchill, and something could also have been done to overcome stagnation in the Maritimes, and to help those Provinces play the part for which their fortunate geographical position seems to fit them. Busy seaports could have been established on the Great Lakes, and new industries encouraged by the power generated in connection with the completion of the St. Lawrence Waterway. These are but a few of the things that Canadians might have done to justify their claim that: "The twentieth century belongs to Canada."

Since only half the century is gone, it may be that Canada, after a somewhat slow start, can set a faster pace during the rest of it. In fact, there is much to suggest this. There are indications that, in the interval, Canadians have attained a greater measure of self-confidence; they have measured their strength against others in two world wars; and they have seen goods produced by them increasingly win their way in the markets of the world. They have seen their representatives grapple with world problems, and hold their own with the brightest from other lands. And they have seen a growing number of their kin attain more than local eminence in the arts and sciences, even though in order to do so too many have been forced to leave Canada.

Most important of all is that Canadians have lately come to appreciate the value of their great northern region. They see now that, instead of being a long, slender strip, Canada also has breadth. They realize that the region they once

considered a wasteland is one of the world's greatest mineral
storehouses; and that in the cataracts and waterfalls of its
numerous northern rivers is concentrated the power of a
hundred million slaves which, properly used, can make Canada one of the great industrial nations of the world. They
know that, whatever the atomic age may have in store, they
possess supplies, the full extent of which is not yet known,
of the materials upon which that age will most likely be
based.

This part of Canada until recently considered worthless
consists chiefly of what is called the Canadian Shield, a U-
shaped region enclosing Hudson Bay on three sides, and
extending from the Labrador coast, across northern Canada,
almost to the Mackenzie Valley. It comprises about 2,500,000
square miles, and occupies more than two-thirds of Canada's
entire area. Generally a plateau of low elevation, its surface
is pitted with depressions providing basins for myriads of
lakes of all sizes and descriptions, connected one to the other
by a maze of tortuous streams. Geologically, it consists
mainly of rocks of Precambrian age, in which valuable
minerals are found wherever they are extensively prospected.

As has been said, no country can be great in this machine
age that does not have an ample supply of the metals upon
which modern industry depends,—iron, copper, lead, zinc,
nickel, and others in less degree. The Canadian Shield is rich
in all these: it produces about 92 per cent of Canada's gold,
56 per cent of her silver, 95 per cent of her copper, and all
her nickel, radium, platinum and cobalt.

Power is also essential. One of the world's largest concen-
trations of oil and natural gas exists in Alberta, extending
northward to the Arctic coast, and eastward into Saskatchewan. Alberta, British Columbia, and the Maritimes contain
important coal deposits. These together with abundant waterpower, especially where farthest from coal and oil, round
out the requirements of a modern industrial nation.

Canada has more than half the world's fresh water, and her

shores are washed by three oceans. She has the longest coast-line of any country in the world, indented by innumerable fine harbours, most of which are still in their natural state. Her fisheries, both salt- and fresh-water, are unsurpassed, and, properly conserved, are inexhaustible. Her timber, if like-wise conserved, will supply the needs of a large population indefinitely. Her agricultural lands, occupied as well as un-occupied, vary in productive capacity, but can supply food for many times her present number of people.

Canada's climate is thought by some to be a serious obstacle,—which it might be in a country less richly en-dowed. In most parts of the country, it cannot be ignored and must be prepared for; but, in the main, the additional operating costs entailed by the long, cold winter which pre-vails over most of Canada are offset by other more favourable factors.

It is often argued that Canada is a geographical anomaly, and that Canadians run counter to natural trends by attempt-ing to develop lines of trade east and west instead of north and south. It is true that the natural lines do not run east and west, but they do run northwest and southeast (except in the far east, where they run northeast and southwest), and they lead *into* the country, not *away* from it. The streams were the furtraders' highways, which took them both to the Arctic and the Pacific, and they still mark the best traffic routes.

Canada is a much more natural unit than many realize. East of the Rockies, the country consists of a great irregular plain, elevated at the outer edges, and sloping gently north-ward, practically all the drainage of which is into the Arctic (which is here taken to include Hudson and James Bays). Very few of Canada's rivers flow southward into the United States, but most flow in the opposite direction. The mighty Mackenzie, which, with its tributaries, is almost as long as the Mississippi (exclusive of the Missouri), flows northwest-ward into the Arctic. The Yukon flows northwestward through Alaska into Bering Sea. The St. Lawrence, draining an immense area on both sides of the International Boundary, flows northeastward to the Atlantic. The Saskatchewan, with its tributaries, draining the greater part of the prairies, empties into Lake Winnipeg, as does the northward-flowing Red; both are drained into Hudson Bay by the Nelson River.

Thus, almost three-quarters of Canada's drainage goes into arctic waters. No mountains or other physiographic barriers separate Canada and the United States along most of the International Boundary, yet the slope of the country is away from the United States; in fact, Canada has her back to the south and faces northward. Although many Canadians do not yet realize it, this is the direction of their future, which will become more and more evident as the centres of population move farther north, and especially with the advance of aviation.

Whether Canadians understand it or not, they are in the grip of events that are re-shaping the world and their position in it. The shortest routes between most points in North America and Eurasia are northward, which means that Canada occupies a more advantageous position in this regard than the United States. If you wish to fly from any point in the United States to almost any point in Eurasia, you will fly over Canada. In flying from New York to Tokyo, for example, a great part of the course is across Canadian territory.

In other respects, Canada is in a favourable geographic position; she adjoins the United States on the south, and the Soviet Union is her northern neighbor, the two most powerful and dynamic countries in the world. (It is assumed here that they will keep from war: any other assumption would render a book about Canada's future almost impossible to write). In Newfoundland, Canada has the two easternmost airports in North America; and her Maritime seaports are a day's sail nearer Europe than any others on the coast; on the west, (except for those in Alaska) her seaports and airports are nearest to China and Japan.

9

While it has been shown here that Canada, in the past fifty years, has not yet attained the position which, at the turn of the century, many expected she should by now have attained, an attempt will be made in this book to show that Canada has all that is required, in a material sense, to make a country great. Even with such resources as shall be described, a nation can, of course, fail to attain greatness; for greatness consists of much more than material success. It is a fair assumption, however, that in these times no country can become really great if it lacks most of the things of which Canada has so great a store; while with such advantages, Canada could become an outstanding nation, and even fulfil Laurier's boast.

Therefore this book will attempt to show that whereas, during most of the first half of the twentieth century, Canada has failed to fulfil early expectations, she can reasonably hope to fulfil them in the remaining half. This assertion is based largely on (1) the existence of the Canadian Shield, with its vast and varied mineral riches, its forests, and its extensive waterpower; (2) the petroleum and natural gas resources of the Great Plains region; and (3) Canada's position in the northern half of North America, rendered strategically important by aviation.

Beginning with a consideration of the new lease of life possible for the Maritimes because of the union of Newfoundland, and the opening up of the Canadian Shield immediately to the north, a description will be given of present developments in the Shield across northern Quebec, Ontario, and the Prairie Provinces, with a forecast of what may be expected in these regions, and their effect, if properly managed, upon the national economy. Continuing westward, an account will be given of the oil and gas developments on the Plains, with a forecast of what may be expected in the region that extends northward to and down the Mackenzie Valley. The importance of the mountains, so often considered a drawback, will also be discussed; and an estimate will be made of the varied possibilities of northern British Columbia, where the last vestiges of the western frontier may still be seen. The immence region comprising Yukon Territory and the Districts of Mackenzie, Keewatin, and Franklin, with their interesting possibilities, will also be described. It is worthy of note that the conquest of this final frontier, whenever it is accomplished, will mark the end of an era that began with Cartier and Champlain.

Descriptions will also be given, and their value to the country will be shown, of the Great Lakes-St. Lawrence Waterway and of the Hudson Bay route. The possibilities will be discussed of air, highway, and rail connections with Asia by way of the Mackenzie and Yukon valleys, and by tunnel under Bering Strait, providing almost the last link in a highway eventually reaching from the tip of Patagonia to Portugal. Such a project is physically possible, only human perversity remains to be overcome.

Finally, consideration will be given to the question as to whether, having provided a high level of prosperity for a much larger population, and having attained a prominent place among the nations of the world, Canada will thereby have achieved greatness. Whether the twentieth century is to be Canada's will depend almost entirely upon the answer to this question.

2

Atlantic Bridgehead

WHEN one of the dreams of the Fathers of Confederation was fulfilled in 1949 by the union of Canada and Newfoundland, the event was of much greater importance than is generally realized. While there was a feeling of satisfaction at what some Canadians considered to be but the return of an area which, despite the Privy Council's decision, should never have been separated from Canada, many others thought of it merely as the addition of a further 152,000 square miles of rock and forest—and some 348,000 people, mostly fisherfolk whose average income was excessively low—to an already over-sized country.

The importance of this event applies more particularly to the Island of Newfoundland itself, rather than to the much larger area in Labrador, valuable though it undoubtedly is. For now that the Island has become part of Canada it completes under a single sovereignty one of the most remarkable maritime regions in the world. Previously, the Maritime Provinces were confined to the southwestern shores of the Gulf of St. Lawrence; the bold Gaspé coast farther north; and the even bolder section of Quebec between the Gulf and Labrador. Newfoundland, forming the eastern side of the quadrangle, was a Crown Colony under separate jurisdiction; and this, even in the most favourable circumstances, imposed certain restrictions upon traffic across the Gulf.

With the inclusion of Newfoundland, however, the Gulf of St. Lawrence becomes virtually a Canadian sea, a much more fitting entry to the Canadian mainland. Furthermore the southeastern coast of Quebec is no longer an outlying sector, and Cape Breton no longer bounded on the east by infinity; both are drawn together into the intimacy of a close family relationship.

To some, this may not seem of much practical value: the Island is still where it always was; and, despite separate political jurisdictions, traffic between it and the Canadian provinces had been almost, if not quite, free. However, there is a difference,—the difference between being a fully-fledged family member and merely a friendly neighbour.

The Gulf of St. Lawrence and the lands surrounding it have geographic advantages such as are possessed by no other region along the Atlantic coast of North America. Where else can be seen so great an expanse of enclosed seaway? Where else does so imposing an entrance lead to so extensive an inland waterway? Where else can so many splendid harbours be found? To these advantages must be added the one mentioned in the previous chapter: this remarkable region lies nearer the great seaports of Europe than does any other part of North America.

This chapter deals mainly with geographic features; the following one will discuss the economic factors that round out the picture. Geographic features are fundamental; and, everything else being equal, are decisive in determining the destiny of a region. That Europe has in many respects outdistanced Asia is not due primarily to any superiority in the genius of her peoples, but rather, among others things, to the geographic fact that her heavily indented coastline and many navigable rivers permitted trade to develop at a time when small boats and timid mariners were the rule, while the same thing was not possible along the Asiatic coast, with its relatively few good harbours and its lack of large rivers.

Nova Scotia and New Brunswick were two of the four original members of the Canadian Confederation. The Intercolonial Railway, opened for traffic between Montreal and

Halifax in 1876, was built to tie these outlying Provinces into the still nebulous Canadian framework. It was a necessity arising out of the geographic situation. Nevertheless, it was toward the vacant regions of the West, for two hundred years under the sway of the Hudson's Bay Company, that the new Government of Canada looked, but the reason was political, rather than geographic. Whether this territory, especially beyond the Rocky Mountains, could be held against the tumultuous onrush of American settlement, which the Mexican Republic had found it impossible to withstand, and from whose feeble grasp Texas and California had already been wrenched, was a matter of great concern to Canadian statesmen.

It was therefore perhaps natural that the Government of Canada should have concentrated its attention upon the development of the West, thus increasing the isolation of the far eastern Provinces. Then, in 1878, the Government of Canada adopted a fiscal policy which, whatever its effects on the national economy as a whole, has undoubtedly worked to the further disadvantage of the Maritime Provinces. Dependent as they were upon fishing, farming, and lumbering, the surplus of which must be sold in the unprotected markets of the world, they were, from then on, compelled to buy what they themselves required in a protected market. While people may differ as to whether the National Policy of 1878 has been of benefit to Canada generally, there is little disagreement as to its effects upon the Maritime Provinces.

The National Policy hastened the decline in Maritime fortunes which began when steel and iron replaced wood in the building of ships. Previous to that, with timber close at hand, with splendid harbours from which to launch ships, and with skilled workmen, it was but natural that shipbuilding should have been an important Maritime industry. In 1865, 294 ships, aggregating over 56,000 tons, and valued at $2,500,000, were built in Nova Scotia; while, in New Brunswick, in the same year, 148 ships, with a total tonnage of more than 65,000, were built. The Maritime Provinces also had the seamen to sail the ships; and wherever ships were afloat, the term Bluenose denoted not only staunch ships, but the hardy and intrepid men who sailed them. The passing of wooden ships marked the end of an era for the Maritimes.

The value of the Maritimes' geographic position was recognized somewhat when the Intercolonial Railway was built, and some years later, when the Canadian Pacific Railway's line through the State of Maine to Saint John, N. B., was completed. While for the greater part of the year, central Canada might act as though the Maritimes counted for very little, Maritime ports came into their own when navigation on the St. Lawrence was closed by ice.

The building, early in the twentieth century, of a second transcontinental railway, with its eastern terminus at Moncton, N. B., and its western terminus at Prince Rupert, B. C., might easily have gone far toward changing the situation in the Maritimes if it had been followed by the settlement and development of the country through which it ran; but, as has already been said, although it provided the shortest route across the continent, it ran mostly through virgin territory, much of it, in the East, across the Canadian Shield, where for many years practically no settlement or other development was attempted.

From time to time, Newfoundland's unique position has been recognized. In 1858, when the first Atlantic cable was finally laid, Newfoundland became its North American terminus; on December 11, 1901, Marconi received the first transatlantic wireless message on Signal Hill, at St. John's; and on June 14, 1919, Alcock and Brown took off on the first transatlantic flight from Lester's Field, near St. John's. Thereafter, Newfoundland was a favourite jumping-off-place for those flying eastward across the Atlantic.

The coming of the second world war brought Newfoundland to the fore. Important military bases were established there by the United States. The Government of Canada built a large airport at Gander, in the northeastern part of the Island, some distance inland; and another was built at Goose Bay, in Labrador, from which to ferry planes across the Atlantic by way of Greenland and Iceland, and to serve as an alternative when flying conditions were less favourable at Gander. Since the war, both airports have continued in use, and Gander especially has become one of the great crossroads of the world.

The Island of Newfoundland is roughly triangular, with an area of 42,734 square miles, consisting of an irregular, rocky plateau sloping from northwest to southeast. Its highest point, Lewis Hill, in the rugged western part, is 2,673 feet high, but its average elevation is about 1,000 feet. The numerous bays and inlets in its 6,000-mile coastline are the remains of sunken valleys; and the ridges of harder rock that have more successfully resisted the action of ice and weather provide backbones for the peninsulas and other projections separating these indentations from one another. Avalon Peninsula, the easternmost point of the Island, is its most important promontory. The peninsula contains about 45 per cent of the Island's people, most of whom live in St. John's the Capital, situated on a land-locked harbour at its northeastern angle.

Newfoundland's narrow-gauge railway, now part of the Canadian National system, begins at Port aux Basques, in the southwestern corner, and follows a northward-sweeping arc across the Island, ending at St. John's.

Labrador, also somewhat triangular, comprises an area 110,000 square miles in extent, occupying almost the whole of the easternmost angle of the North American continent. It is shaped so peculiarly because the Privy Council confirmed the contention of the Newfoundland Government that it should include all the land in the Atlantic watershed. Hamilton River rises some 320 miles from the coast, and thus the boundary line makes a considerable detour in order to follow the height of land. North of the Hamilton basin, the height of land gradually approaches the sea, until at Cape Chidley, where Hudson Strait begins, Labrador tapers to a point.

Most of Labrador consists of undulating plateau, similar to other parts of the Canadian Shield. Its general elevation is about 2,000 feet, but along the coast the land rises, and the Torngat Mountains in the north reach elevations of nearly 6,000 feet. The coastline is much broken by inlets of all shapes and sizes, somewhat resembling those along the British Columbia coast, except that the heights framing them, while much lower, are bare of trees. Hamilton Inlet, about 200 miles north of the Strait of Belle Isle, together with Melville Lake, constitutes one of the most important indentations on the coast. Hamilton Inlet itself extends inland for about 40 miles, and is connected by a narrow channel about 10 miles long with Melville Lake, continuing westward for another 125 miles.

Hamilton River, whose watershed comprises about 29,900 square miles, is potentially one of the most important rivers on the Atlantic seaboard. It consists of two sections of entirely different types; the upper one, similar to most streams in the Canadian Shield, has no well-defined valley, but seems to flow almost on the surface, spreading into numerous deeply-indented, island-studded lakes, and dividing frequently into a number of separate channels, all broken by rapids and waterfalls. In some places, it flows into a lake by more than one inlet, and leaves by more than one outlet. In the second section, which begins about 200 miles above its mouth, Hamilton River entirely changes its ways. Instead of meandering through a succession of shallow lakes and lake-expansions, it drops suddenly into its ancient channel, cut deep into the bedrock, in which it continues until it empties into Melville Lake.

In its descent from the tableland level to its old channel, the river drops a total of 1,038 feet in 16 miles. This descent begins in a series of heavy rapids, continuing so for about four miles, and then, at Grand Falls, the river, rushing down a narrow, rocky chute, plunges into a seething cauldron 245 feet below, the roar and spray of which can be heard and seen for many miles. The drop here is nearly 100 feet higher than Niagara's famed Horseshoe Fall. Below the falls, the river races for 12 tortuous miles through Bowdoin Canyon, making a further descent of 574 feet, where vertical walls rise 400 feet, and in places are not more than 100 yards apart. In these 16 miles, the Hamilton River provides one of the world's most stupendous spectacles.

It can thus be said that the lands bordering the Gulf have advantages possessed by no other region along the Atlantic coast of North America. They lie off the entrance to the world's greatest waterway, to which more than half the population of Canada is tributary, with an additional 40 millions immediately to the south. They have many excellent harbours, of which Halifax, Sydney, and Gaspé Basin are among the finest in the world. There are so many, in fact, that their value is often overlooked. In not many places, if at all, are there so many neglected harbours; and one has only to think of regions less fortunate to realize how valuable at least some of these harbours must some day become.

Harbours are of little value, however, if ships do not frequent them; and ships will not do so if there is not enough traffic. Cargoes will not be available unless the country back of the harbours provides homes for many people to produce goods for exchange. In the next chapter, we shall see what resources these lands bordering the Gulf have to offer as an attraction to those without whom busy seaports and factories are not possible.

3

Signs of Dawn in the East

COAL and iron lay beneath the soil of Great Britain for ages, yet had little influence upon the existing agricultural economy. It was not till near the end of the eighteenth century, when technological science had made some advances, that these resources were more fully put to use and the Industrial Revolution began. Since that day, iron and steel rather than agriculture have been the basis of civilization, not only in Great Britain, but throughout the world. That humanity has failed to reap anything like the full possibilities of civilization, and that so much of what it has produced has been diverted to destructive ends, is not in itself a condemnation of the iron and steel era. The potentiality of this era for human welfare is infinitely greater than its capacity for destruction; it is good or bad only in accordance with the uses that are made of it.

The lands bordering the Gulf have now a chance to inaugurate in their part of the world a period of advancement such as rarely falls to the lot of any community. Iron ore from the Wabana mines, on Bell Island, Conception Bay, near St. John's, and coal mined at Glace Bay and Sydney Mines, Cape Breton, supply the iron and steel mills of the Dominion Steel and Coal Corporation at Sydney, the leading Maritime industry. So far, however, this industry has had little influence upon the basic economy of a region still characterized by small-scale primary producers, such as fishermen, farmers, and lumbermen, although fish-processing and pulp and paper production are increasingly important. It must be freely admitted, too, that the scale of living which

19

the coal and steel economy has hitherto provided leaves much to be desired.

Ever since the Ice Cap retreated from the eastern end of the Canadian Shield, exposing a great red scar stretching at intervals from near the headwaters of the Hamilton River to the shore of Ungava Bay, huge deposits of rich iron ore have awaited the day when Man should come in search of them. These deposits are chiefly in what is known as the Labrador Trough, extending northwestward for about 400 miles, with an average width of about 30 miles.

Dr. A. P. Low, one of the most brilliant of that group of men of science and action who under the *aegis* of the Geological Survey of Canada have achieved a record of exploration unexcelled in any other land, spent several years in Labrador and Ungava during the last decade of the nineteenth century. Almost half a century elapsed, however, before the modest records of his remarkable journeys became required reading for geologists and others seeking new sources of iron ore, and by financiers in many of the world's money markets. If the great Mesabi Iron Range in northern Minnesota were not about to become exhausted, but had another half-century of life, it is safe to say that this new interest might not have developed so soon; but the end of Mesabi Range is in sight, and the steel industry in the United States is forced to look elsewhere for its future source of supply.

In 1936, a concession was granted by the Government of the Province of Quebec to a Montreal group, whose interest was acquired in 1942 by Hollinger Consolidated Gold Mines Limited, whose principal property is at Timmins, Ontario, giving that company the exclusive exploration rights over an area of 3,900 square miles adjoining the Quebec-Newfoundland boundary. At the same time, the Newfoundland Government granted a similar concession covering 20,000 square miles of adjacent territory in Labrador. The

original group were interested chiefly in prospecting for gold or other valuable minerals; their attention was turned to iron only after the geologists had reported widespread evidence of that metal.

The concessions are held by Hollinger North Shore Exploration Corporation Limited, which controls the 3,900 square miles secured from the Quebec Government, and Labrador Mining and Exploration Company Limited, which controls the 20,000 square miles in Labrador. In each of these, the M. A. Hanna Company, of Cleveland, Ohio, experienced in the iron and steel business, has a minority interest. The Quebec, North Shore and Labrador Railway Company was incorporated to build and operate a railway from Knob Lake, beyond the northern part of the Labrador concession, to Seven Islands, a port on the north shore of the Gulf of St. Lawrence, 360 miles to the south. The townsite of Burnt Creek and an airfield were laid out at the north end of the line, with a seaplane base at Knob Lake.

Subsequently, the Iron Ore Company of Canada, with an authorized capital of $170,000,000, was incorporated under the laws of Delaware to provide the necessary financing. In addition to the Hollinger-Hanna interests, those involved in the transaction include several of the largest American steel companies, exclusive of United States Steel. Another new company, Hollinger-Hanna Limited, was incorporated in Canada to manage the Canadian end of the business for the Iron Ore Company of Canada.

In the interval, drilling was undertaken at a number of points, and extensive deposits of high-grade hematite ore were disclosed, most of which can be mined by open-pit methods. Much of the ore stands in ridges, in many places high above the general level, and can be loaded directly into cars on tracks strung along the bases of the ridges. According to the latest accounts, the drills show deposits in excess of 400 million tons, and it is believed that this is but a portion of the ore actually available. Surface showings only were

hrough, Newfoundland Fishing Village

tested for a distance of 90 miles; intervening sections hidden by overburden were left for later examination. In one place, when a churn-drill was being tried out, ore was struck under two feet of overburden, and the drill was still in ore when drilling stopped at a depth of over 360 feet. This would suggest that similar deposits are likely to be found at other places along the Trough where no surface signs exist.

In addition to hematite ore, which runs as high as 68 per cent iron, large deposits of manganiferous ore have been found. In some places, the manganese content is sufficient to justify classification as manganese ore which, if found in quantity, is extremely important, since no other extensive manganese deposits have been found in Canada. Thus, the lands bordering on the Gulf can provide all the requirements for the manufacture of high-grade steel.

In 1946, the Quebec Government granted the rights on 1,500 square miles of territory immediately north of the Hollinger concession to Norancon Exploration Limited, controlled by Noranda Mines Limited in association with two other large mining companies. North of this concession, the exploration rights on 1,000 square miles were granted to Fort Chimo Mines Limited, controlled by Frobisher Limited, a subsidiary of Ventures Limited. Farther north, the Quebec-Labrador Development Company has 1,000 square miles; north of this, Fenimore Iron Mines has 448 square miles, constituting what is believed to be the final portion of the Labrador Trough. Ore from that portion of the Trough within reach of Ungava Bay may possibly be taken to market by sea. With the exception of the Hollinger concession, all those referred to here are wholly within the Province of Quebec; exclusive exploration rights are for certain periods, after which the companies must indicate the areas they wish to develop, when the remaining territory will revert to the public domain.

The Kaniapiskau River, which runs parallel to the Trough, tumbling over numerous falls and cataracts, can supply power for all requirements. The falls at Eaton Canyon are thus described by Low:

> . . . again narrowing to 100 feet it [the river] falls thirty feet into a narrow rocky gorge, . . . and turning directly south, rushes down between jagged perpendicular walls with a width varying from fifty to one hundred and fifty feet. As the stream descends, the banks rise and become 200 feet high a quarter of a mile below the first fall. Here the river turns sharply to the northeast and continues as a rushing torrent, through a deeper and still narrower gorge, with overhanging walls of red granite on the east side. The overhang is so great that a stone dropped from the top of this side would almost reach the foot of the opposite cliff when it struck the water 350 feet below. After falling in this manner for a third of a mile, the river widens to a hundred yards, and changing its direction to the east, descends less abruptly for a quarter of a mile, while the walls of the canyon are a hundred feet lower, and much less abrupt. Next, turning north, it makes a direct fall of a hundred feet into a circular basin about fifty yards in diameter. Nothing but seething water and foam is seen in this rocky basin, which resembles a gigantic boiling cauldron. A small brook, on the north side, also falls into the basin, descending the perpendicular wall in a cascade 200 feet in height. The river leaves the basin by a rocky channel, rushing out with a fall of thirty feet in immense waves that gradually subside in a second and larger circular basin at its foot, where it widens to 150 yards. . .

This river was originally to have supplied power for the iron mines, but another was later chosen. It is not likely, however, that the energy of the falls at Eaton Canyon will run to waste indefinitely.

The railway, construction of which was begun late in 1950, consists of single-track with many sidings; but, if, as is expected, 20 million tons of ore a year are eventually shipped over it, double-track will, of course, be necessary. A maximum grade of 0.3 per cent, southbound, has been secured, which will allow for heavy loads requiring a minimum of power. A deepwater port capable of accommodating ocean-going ships has been surveyed at Seven Islands, and ample space for ore-bins and docks is available. Seven Islands should in time become an important seaport.

The Hollinger interests expect to spend a total of about $200 million, which will include about $50 million for the railway; $45 million for railway equipment; $7 million for a power plant; and $10 million for ore-bins and docks at Seven Islands.

The United States market makes the development of Labrador iron ore possible. Not only are existing steel concerns interested, but the proximity of Labrador has induced New England industrialists to consider the establishment of steel mills on Atlantic tidewater. It is stated that Labrador iron ore can be unloaded at Boston or New London more cheaply than the lower-grade Mesabi Range ore can now reach Cleveland or Pittsburgh. Boston is only 1,000 miles from Seven Islands as against 1,400 for Pittsburgh.

If it is good business for New England to initiate an iron and steel industry based on Labrador ore, how much easier would it be for Canadians to build plants much nearer the source of supply? New England has no coal and must haul it by sea or by rail; but, in the Maritime Provinces, ore can be taken directly to Cape Breton coal, or to Pictou, New Glasgow, or a number of other places on the Nova Scotia mainland. Coal from the Minto Basin in New Brunswick could also be utilized.

In addition to the above, the possibilities inherent in the Hamilton Inlet-Melville Lake area should not be overlooked. It is estimated that about 4,475,000 horsepower can be developed in the 16-mile section of Hamilton River comprising Grand Fall, the rapids above, and the canyon below, with 1,130,000 horsepower at Muskrat Falls, about 18 miles above the mouth of the river. Other falls are estimated as capable of supplying an additional 1,000,000 horsepower, making a total for Hamilton River of about 7,000,000 horsepower, or about half as much as Canada's entire hydro-electric installation at the present time.

Although unavailable during a large part of the year because of ice, Hamilton Inlet, since it is nearest to northern Europe of any North American port, may some day provide a useful outlet. With Melville Lake, it permits ocean-going ships to penetrate 165 miles inland, and this is only about 140 miles east of the iron ore deposits now under development by the Hollinger interests. A wide gravel terrace extending far into Melville Lake has resulted from material brought down by the river, and here, on an upper terrace, Goose Airport has been built. Within easy reach of Melville Lake are stretches of fine timber, some large enough for lumber, with enough small stuff to support pulp and paper mills. There is a good chance that iron deposits nearer than those now being worked, or other minerals, may be found. With these resources, actual and potential, it should be possible to develop an industrial centre somewhere near the mouth of Hamilton River, an opportunity which Canadians can hardly afford to overlook if they are to make good their claim to the twentieth century.

Besides new iron and steel mills for the Maritimes, it is not unreasonable to predict other industries based on these metals. One possible industry should, at least, be mentioned. As we have seen, the Maritimes once built ships for all the world. That trade ended, not because Bluenose shipwrights had lost the shipbuilding art, but because, owing to the growing use of steel, of which the Maritimes had none, they could no longer meet the demand. Now, with steel at their very doors, with their efficient workmen, and with their many fine harbours, it should not be too difficult for Maritime shipbuilders to recapture the position they once held.

The steel industry, while perhaps the most important, is not the only one that the Precambrian rocks of the Canadian Shield can make available to the people bordering on the

25

Canada's Century

Gulf. Copper is found at several places on the northeast coast of Newfoundland; and for many years copper, lead, and zinc concentrates have been shipped, mostly to European countries, from the Buchans mine in the north-central part of the Island. More recently, zinc and copper concentrates have been shipped from the Gaspé Peninsula, and exploratory operations by Noranda Mines Limited and others have recently disclosed immense deposits of copper in Gaspé which will most likely require the building of a smelter in that region.

Deposits of base metals have been found at a number of places in Labrador and Ungava, too far from market to be of commercial use; and now that a railway is penetrating that region, and will, in all probability be extended as need arises, the chances for base metal production there are extremely good. At present, the nearest copper refinery is at Montreal, and consequently the establishment of another somewhere in the Maritime region might sooner or later become a feasible proposition.

One more new industry may be mentioned. At Allard Lake, 22 miles inland from Havre St. Pierre, on the north shore of the Gulf, a large deposit of ilmenite is being developed by Kennco Exploration Limited, subsidiary of Kennecott Copper Corporation. Ilmenite is a titanium-bearing ore, consisting in this case of from 30 to 40 per cent titanium and 40 per cent iron. Development was begun in 1946, since when drilling has shown the existence of upward of 200 million tons of ore. A railway, 27 miles in length, has been built to connect Allard Lake with Havre St. Pierre, which is north of Anticosti Island.

Kennecott Copper Corporation, in association with New Jersey Zinc Company, has worked out a process for treating ilmenite. The ore is fused in an electrical furnace, separating the iron, which is recovered as pig iron; the titanium is then concentrated in a slag carrying about 70 per cent

26

titanium. Kennecott Copper Corporation has created two subsidiaries: Allard Lake (Quebec) Mines Limited, to operate the mine; and Quebec Iron and Titanium Corporation, to operate a smelter at Sorel, 50 miles below Montreal, which has a daily capacity of 1,500 tons.

Present plans call only for the production of titanium oxide pigment (in addition to 150 tons of iron a day); but later, when a practicable process has been devised, it is hoped to produce titanium in metal form, hitherto produced only experimentally. Titanium oxide, in the form of titanium white, is used in the manufacture of paint; to render paper opaque; to make rubber white; and to delustre artificial silk. It is also used in the manufacture of ceramics, printing inks, linoleum, and cosmetics. Previously, all titanium products used in Canada were imported from the United States, but now, of course, Canada is an exporter.

Certain forms of titanium are also used in the treatment of special steels. Titanium metal could be used for many things, especially where light weight, great tensile strength, and resistance to high temperatures are concerned; and when its production is economically possible the value of the Quebec deposits will be greatly increased. The lands bordering the Gulf have the facilities necessary to take advantage of this new industry; in fact, it is probable that, especially to serve world markets, a site for a smelter somewhere farther east might supplement the one at Sorel.

The pulp and paper industry could be extended considerably in the lands bordering the Gulf. The two large plants on the Island of Newfoundland are owned by British firms, which between them control most of the Island's available pulp lands, and it is not likely that any other large plant would find it profitable to establish there. The first plant built, owned by Anglo-Newfoundland Development Company Limited, controlled by the Northcliffe newspaper interests, began operations in 1909 at Grand Falls, on the Exploits

River, in the northeastern part of the Island. The other plant was established in 1923 at Corner Brook, at the mouth of the Humber River, on the west coast. This project was beset by financial difficulties almost from the first; but in 1937 Bowater's Newfoundland Pulp and Paper Mills Limited bought control, and since then the plant, equipped with the most modern machinery, has become one of the largest producers of pulp and paper in the world.

Newfoundland-Labrador, as already mentioned, contains a considerable amount of pulpwood adjacent to the Hamilton River and its tributaries; and it is estimated that at least two large plants could be supplied. While the climate, on the coast, is unpleasant, it becomes much milder a short distance inland: at any rate, the resources of the region are undoubtedly sufficient to compensate for any disadvantages due to climate.

Pulp mills are already in operation at a number of places on the north shore of the Gulf, where both power and pulpwood are available. With the increased transportation facilities that such ports as Seven Islands and Havre St. Pierre will make available, other mills may be expected along the coast. A mill could probably be operated on the Gaspé Peninsula, supplied by timber from the peninsula itself, from Anticosti Island, or from the north shore of the Gulf. In many places along the north shore stands of merchantable timber could support sawmills, especially since mining and other activity in the region could be expected to provide a steady market.

The pulp and paper industry of New Brunswick does not yet consume all available pulpwood, and further mills are possible in that province. This might be an advantage to those already established, since increased production often makes for better transportation and marketing facilities. Nova Scotia, although now possessing much less timber than New Brunswick, could also increase her pulp and paper production somewhat. The rocky region along the south coast, with its many streams flowing into the Atlantic, provides favorable conditions for the growth of trees; and with reforestation and proper protection of existing forests, Nova Scotia should be able to provide indefinitely for a considerable pulp and paper industry.

These industries, with their secondary manufacturing, would make necessary an increase in the population which, in turn, would help to provide new markets for existing industries. The potato-growers of Prince Edward Island and New Brunswick, and the apple-growers of Annapolis, might find a ready market for their produce in Labrador, where agricultural possibilities are limited. This, for the apple-growers, would supplement the British market which has not always been as consistent as might be desired. Fishermen would also benefit by enlarged markets.

Fishing and lumbering, however, may not derive sufficient benefit from these new developments to enable those engaged in them to maintain a scale of living equivalent to that which industrial workers might attain. The heavy industries may best be managed by large corporations, especially if the public interest be well guarded; but fishing and farming must to a large extent continue to be conducted in a small way; and the only manner in which the individual can get the benefit of large-scale operations is by co-operating with others whose problems are similar.

The most successful experiment in co-operation on the continent, known as the "St. Francis Xavier Experiment," about which several books and many articles have been written, has been developed in the Maritimes. It grew principally out of the interest of three men at St. Francis Xavier University at Antigonish, Nova Scotia,—Dr. James Tomkins, Dr. Michael Coady, and A. B. MacDonald. Dr. Coady is the director of the extension department of the university, and it is his department that has been largely responsible for the movement. As stated by Dr. A. E. Corbett, Director of the

Canadian Association for Adult Education, this movement "has substantially changed the economic and social life of the working people of eastern Nova Scotia and in so doing has set a standard of economic and social values for the co-operative movement all over the continent." (Toronto *Saturday Night*, Sept. 20, 1949).

Mining has been called a wasting industry and, at best, destined eventually to come to an end; the pulp and paper industry, unless conservation is rigorously practised, may also be put in the same category; but scenery is a resource that may be exploited forever without any lessening of supply. In this, the lands bordering the Gulf have a priceless asset, whether it be the rugged grandeur of the Newfoundland and Labrador shores; the bold panoramas of Cape Breton; the breath-taking vistas of Gaspé Peninsula; the infinite variety of the coasts of the Nova Scotia mainland and New Brunswick; or the restful reaches of Prince Edward Island.

People go from all over the world to the Swiss Alps, and from all parts of North America to the Laurentians of Old Quebec for winter sports; and it is conceivable that the day may come when the hills which form the height of land, almost overlooking the Gulf's north shore, will also have their thousands of devotees. Here is a winter playground within easy reach of the Maritime Provinces, and the large American cities farther south.

It may seem presumptuous to suggest, as is done here, that these Maritime Provinces, so long the Cinderellas of Canada, should suddenly step forth into a front-rank position among the world's industrial regions. It is not the intention to create such an impression; but it is asserted, nevertheless, that the opportunity does exist. The building of an industry requires time, and much opposition can be expected from rival centres; established lines of trade, and connections formed through long association, are slow to change; yet, in

Eaton Canyon, Kaniapiskau Ri

the long run, availability of raw materials and power, coupled with favourable geographical position, must, if due advantage be taken of them, make themselves felt.

An attempt has been made to show that, like other parts of Canada, the Maritimes have an opportunity to draw upon the vast resources of the Canadian Shield which, in the final analysis, is one of the chief repositories of Canada's greatness. As will be shown later, much of the wealth that has come to the people of Canada has been contributed in one form or another by the Canadian Shield. How the people of the Maritimes will take advantage of their opportunity, only the future can tell.

ane Base, Knob Lake, Que.

4

Where Past and Future Meet

FOR a century and a half, Canada, as New France, consisted almost entirely of a narrow strip along the St. Lawrence River. And although Canada has since spread to the Atlantic and the Pacific, that strip along the St. Lawrence is still what most people think of as Quebec. Yet when one glances at the map and notes the great extent of the Province, shaped (including Labrador) like a giant arrowhead, or perhaps an upended ham, one wonders whether the tiny portion that is Old Quebec will, in time, leaven the lump; or whether this immense northern region will not in the end succeed in placing its stamp on the older part as well. If this should happen, it may be that what has constituted Quebec in the past—and still largely does—will cease to exist outside of history books. The land has always moulded the people, and not people the land; this new land that must now be conquered will surely mould its people into different patterns from those of the past. The British Conquest is looked upon as the point from which time is counted forward and back; but the present moment, poised as it is on the threshold of an era to be shaped by the exigencies of the Canadian Shield, may some day be counted a much more definite break between past and future than any other in the history of Quebec.

In the past, the opening-up of new country has been on an individual basis; men have gone from the settlements to make their homes in the nearby wilderness, supporting themselves by trapping, planting crops, or cutting timber. Thus settlement inched its way into new areas; but this cannot be done in the Canadian Shield. The new economy will be geared to the extraction of wealth from deep within the earth's crust. Development of this sort cannot be carried on by a gradual process, because mineral occurrences are not continuous, or even contiguous; in one region there may be a group of copper mines; in another, lead and zinc mines, or deposits of ilmenite or iron ore. Interspersed, will be gold mines. For this reason, people will live in relatively large communities, rather than on small farm holdings,—and these will need to be planned. Cities and towns in the Shield will not grow sporadically as in the older communities, and will require much more organization than ever before.

This situation is not peculiar to New Quebec; it applies everywhere across the extent of the Shield, from Labrador to Great Bear Lake; and when the era now beginning is well established, it will most likely be seen that the Canadian Shield has left its imprint, not only upon Quebec, but upon all Canada.

In 1912, the region previously known as Ungava was added to what was then the Province of Quebec, bringing its area to 594,860 square miles, the largest in Canada. Although this huge addition was made early in the century, very little has since been done to change its primeval condition. It is still largely a wilderness, inhabited mainly by Indians, Eskimos, and trappers of white or mixed blood. Its principal settlements—except for relatively recent ones being built in the iron regions—consist of trading posts, to which, as they have done for almost 300 years, native and other trappers bring their furs. Most of these, like Rupert House and Fort George, are at the estuaries of large rivers, but a few are inland.

The climate of New Quebec is not really as terrible as is sometimes imagined. It ranges from temperate to very cold, depending upon latitude and distance from the sea. The direction of the wind has much to do with the weather. South and southwest winds, common in summer, generally bring overcast skies and sometimes drizzling rain. When the wind shifts to the north or northwest, clearer weather and lower temperatures may be expected. Heavy snow or cold rains usually come with a northeast wind; and when the wind is from the east or southeast, the weather is mostly clear and pleasant. In winter, the snowfall varies from three to six feet.

The rivers, racing along their rocky channels, do not carry much silt, but some of them have built up fairly extensive alluvial flats in their lower reaches, in some of which farming is possible on a limited scale. In a few places, particularly about the southern end of James Bay, garden produce has been raised successfully for many years; but, generally speaking, the region as a whole has not much to offer the farmer. It may well be, however, that further plant experimentation will extend the area over which some farming is possible. The difficulty is not entirely due to climate: over large areas of the Canadian Shield there is so little soil that patches large enough to call a farm are not easy to find; and even where the soil is not too thin, it is, because of the nature of the underlying rocks, and other contributing factors, of low fertility.

The greater part of the southern portion, as far north as latitude 54° N., is fairly heavily forested, except for the summits of rocky hills, which are usually bare of anything but shrubs and mosses. The timber is suited chiefly for pulpwood, but, here and there, especially in the valleys of rivers draining into the St. Lawrence, considerable quantities of timber large enough for lumber may be found. The principal trees are black spruce, white spruce, balsam fir, tamarack, banksian pine, white or yellow birch, aspen poplar, and balsam poplar. Northward of latitude 54, treeless areas increase, both as regards number and extent. In these parts, wooded areas are found principally about the margins of small lakes and in river-valleys, and the trees are also smaller. Then, near the southern end of Ungava Bay, they disappear altogether, and are succeeded by grass- and moss-covered tundra, or prairie.

As in the greater part of the Canadian Shield, the lakes and streams of New Quebec are filled with fish, mainly lake trout, which run up to 50 or 60 pounds, and whitefish averaging from three to four pounds. A species of small sturgeon is caught in some of the lakes and streams, while Atlantic salmon are found in rivers flowing into Ungava Bay, but, for some reason, are not found in streams emptying into Hudson Bay. Land-locked salmon, or *ouananiche*, are found in lakes and streams where high waterfalls cut off access to the sea. Brook trout are caught in many places, the sea-run variety, found about the mouths of rivers, often weighing up to 14 pounds. Hearne's salmon, or arctic trout, are common along the northern part of the east shore of Hudson Bay; and codfish are plentiful along the coast to the bottom of James Bay.

The Province of Quebec stretches northward a thousand miles to Hudson Strait, which is farther than the northern boundary of any other province. About 200 miles north of Montreal, the National Transcontinental line of the CNR crosses from east to west. Not long ago, those travelling this line saw nothing but wilderness in every direction, and, although much of it is still wilderness, it now skirts the northern edge of a mining region whose extent no one knows. The railway was not responsible for this development, which spread eastward from Ontario, following the building of the Temiskaming & Northern Ontario Railway (now Ontario Northland), as described in a later chapter. From Noranda and Rouyn a belt of territory stretches eastward, dotted with the headframes of mines, both gold and base-metal, in all stages of development, and containing such towns as Cadillac, Malartic, Bourlemaque, and Val d'Or.

Val d'Or is an example of the new type of mining town that in the next few years will be found scattered along the northern frontier. Not long since it was hacked out of the bush, its shacks jostle modern business blocks on its mile-long principal street. It has garish eating, drinking, and dancing places, but also has an up-to-date high school building and a fine hospital. Its upwards of 10,000 inhabitants are preponderantly unattached males who work steadily at good wages, and whose recreational needs set their stamp upon the social life of the community.

Chibougamau, which to the Indians means "Land of Promise," lying about 200 miles northeast of Val d'Or, may be the next spot to flare into public notice. For many years it has fired the imaginations of both prospectors and financiers. It hummed with activity in 1936, when several hundred mining claims were staked, and some of the largest mining companies in Canada got their hands on what looked like promising gold and copper properties, but Chibougamau was then too far away. The nearest settled spot is the region about Lake St. John, some 150 miles to the southeast; and this gap was bridged near the end of 1949 when an all-weather highway was completed from St. Felicien, on the CNR near Lake St. John, to Chibougamau. A few months later the Quebec Government announced that the road would be extended northward to Waconichi Lake, in the Mistassini Lake drainage system. A townsite has been surveyed on the shore of Lake Gillman, not far from Chibougamau Lake, and on July 4, 1950, the first commercial lots were sold by auction, bringing from $1,000 to $4,200 each. An airstrip has been laid out, forerunner of the airport to be. The need for a railway is already evident, and the advantages of different routes are being eagerly advanced by groups of rival advocates. The Aluminum Company of Canada has decided to develop power on the Peribonka River, some of which will be available for Chibougamau mines, several of which have already begun underground operations for which electric power is the cheapest and most convenient.

Although Chibougamau is 325 miles north of Montreal, and seems to be quite far north, it is still farther south than

the greater part of Canada. And even when Chibougamau
and the intervening area are fully developed, most of New
Quebec will be still untapped, with about seven-eighths of it
for the future to develop. It is a land of large rivers, such as
the Koksoak and the George, flowing northward into Ungava
Bay, or the Great Whale, Eastmain, and Rupert, flowing into
Hudson or James Bays. Most of these rivers tumble down
cataracts or over falls, thus providing possible power for the
development of the country's natural wealth.

Now that attention is being turned toward New Quebec,
development is likely to occur in a number of widely separated places. Richmond Gulf, an interesting indentation in the
eastern shore of Hudson Bay, about latitude 56° N., may be
one of these. Triangular in shape, 23 miles from south to
north, and 19 miles wide at its base, the inlet is separated
from Hudson Bay by a ridge of rock from 500 to 1,200 feet
high and about two miles wide, through which a narrow
opening, called The Hazard, in places only 300 yards wide,
leads to the waters outside.

The rocks surrounding Richmond Gulf are somewhat
similar to those in the Ungava Trough, while nearby are the
Belcher Islands, known to contain important iron ore deposits. Evidences of lead, zinc, copper, and other minerals
have been found which some day might render the region
one of great importance, especially since two rivers, falling
over cliffs in their descent from the plateau, could provide
immense quantities of power. The Wiachouan River has a
sheer drop of 315 feet within a mile of its mouth, and a
second fall a mile upstream has a head of 65 feet; while the
Clearwater, in its final 50 miles, descends 750 feet. Princess
Falls on Little Whale River have a drop of 164 feet. Although
tidal currents rushing through The Hazard make entrance
difficult at some stages of tide, Richmond Gulf could provide
deepwater shelter for ocean-going ships.

In 1942, Gulf Lead Mines Limited secured a concession
from the Quebec Government granting exclusive exploration

rights on 445 square miles, extending for 60 miles along the Hudson Bay coast, both north and south of Richmond Gulf. In subsequent years, geological and geophysical surveys were conducted and about 60,000 feet of diamond drilling was done near the mouth of Little Whale River. This proved the existance of immense deposits of lead-zinc ore, but of a grade that would not permit operation under present conditions of transportation. They provide, however, valuable reserves for the future.

The possibilities of New Quebec may be gauged by what has been done in other parts of the Canadian Shield. The St. Maurice River, a typical Shield stream, rises in the divide between the St. Lawrence Valley and the Hudson Bay watershed, flowing in a southeasterly direction to join the St. Lawrence at Three Rivers.

As recently as 1900, the St. Maurice was untamed and un- used over the whole of its 325 miles. Except at its mouth, there was practically no settlement along it, and except for a little lumbering and trapping, no industry. Practically all of its drainage area was heavily forested, and most of the country, unsuitable for agriculture, seemed likely to remain exclusively devoted to the growing of trees. Since the headwaters were in fairly flat country, dotted with lakes, making ideal conditions for storage, the river seemed well suited to power development.

At the turn of the century a group of men organized the Shawinigan Water and Power Company to harness some of the river's energy at a cataract called Shawinigan, 21 miles above Three Rivers. At first great difficulty was experienced in financing the project because no market existed for power in that wilderness, and to transmit power the 100 miles to Montreal seemed a wild dream. By the promise of cheap power, however, the promoters were able to induce an aluminum company to build a plant at Shawinigan Falls, and they themselves formed a company to build a plant for the manufacture of calcium carbide. On the strength of power contracts with these industries sufficient capital was secured to finance the construction of a powerhouse containing two 5,000 horsepower units. This installation was completed in 1902, and the next step was the building of a line to transmit power to Montreal.

From these small beginnings has grown one of the great industrial districts in the world. Cheap electrical power attracted many industries to the area—immense plants now produce aluminum, newsprint, textiles, chemicals, plastics, metal products, and many other derivatives of Quebec's natural resources, which are sold in markets in many parts of the world. Behind all this is the energy of the St. Maurice River, which a few short years ago was wasting its strength in a turbulent, untamed descent from the Canadian Shield to the St. Lawrence.

Now the river is almost completely controlled. The Gouin Dam, about 240 miles above Three Rivers, has transformed the headwaters into an immense reservoir with a storage-capacity of 280 million cubic feet. This dam stores the waters of spring for use in the low-water season so that an even flow may be provided for the plants below. Growing out of the original 10,000-horsepower plant of 1902, the Shawinigan Water and Power Company and its subsidiaries now own six plants on the river with an installed capacity of 1,610,400 horsepower, and there remain four sites yet to be developed. The harnessing of these four additional sites together with extensions to the present plants will add another 469,500 horsepower, making the eventual installation on the river close to 2,400,000 horsepower.

Thus a wilderness of yesterday has become a rich valley; towns have grown up around industry, and over the countryside the population prospers by the use of electric power. This is typical of what power in the Canadian Shield can perform when raw materials and transportation are available.

A development of almost equal importance in the Quebec portion of the Shield, indicative of what may yet be expected in other parts, is that on the Saguenay River. The great gash in the rocks now known as the Saguenay River existed for many ages before the Glacial Period, but was probably not so deep as it later became. That a river should have a depth of 800 feet—far below the level of the sea,—seems almost unbelievable, yet such is the depth of the Saguenay. When the glaciers were pushing across the hard rocky surface of the Canadian Shield, this ancient river-bed was filled with ice which, as the vast icesheet moved, became a sort of giant ploughshare, gouging the channel even deeper. When at length the ice began to melt, retreating slowly northward, a great moraine was deposited across the upper part of the valley behind which a large lake was impounded.

In the course of time, thick layers of sand and mud brought down by streams from the still-melting ice farther north were deposited. These alluvial deposits are now fertile fields providing homes for prosperous farmers; the lake, now much reduced, is called St. John. The deep Saguenay channel extends only 50 miles back from the St. Lawrence River; and in the 30 miles above that point the river occupies a shallow rocky channel in which it tumbles over one cataract after another, dropping 330 feet in the descent from the tableland to the level of the deep Saguenay channel. In this respect, it resembles somewhat the Hamilton, in Labrador.

The lands about Lake St. John first attracted hardy Canadien settlers; but earlier than that trappers seeking the pelts of fur-bearing animals knew the country well. Chicoutimi, at the head of the deep channel, was one of the first settlements. Later, the unharnessed energy in the upper Saguenay tempted men to put it to work.

Aluminum is one of the commonest ingredients of the earth's crust, but is usually so thinly distributed that it is of no value, and only in a few places is it yet found in sufficient quantities to be of use. One of these is in British Guiana, where immense deposits of bauxite, as aluminum ore is called, are found within easy reach of tidewater. Once on board ship, it can be transported to wherever there is the power to smelt it into aluminum ingots. Great heat is necessary, and for this electrical furnaces are most satisfactory. In 1901, an aluminum plant was built at Shawinigan Falls, as already mentioned, where aluminum was made for the first time in Canada; but as the use of aluminum increased, the capacity of this plant was insufficient. In looking about for a more suitable site, the Aluminum Company of Canada turned to the Saguenay.

The Saguenay was suitable from every standpoint; power could be developed within easy access of the sea, and the raw materials could be brought to the power. In addition to bauxite, cryolite, which comes from Greenland, and petroleum coke, which comes mainly from Texas, are needed, and these come direct to the Saguenay by ship. Furthermore, Saguenay is close to the United States and Canadian markets, through which the markets of the world can be reached.

The first dam, powerhouse (with a capacity of 540,000 horsepower), and aluminum plant were built in 1926 at Isle Maligne, not far below the outlet of Lake St. John. The next powerhouse, Shipshaw No. 1, was built 20 miles below at a spot where the swiftness of the water made dam-building almost impossible, but the ingenuity of the engineers was equal to the task. They first built cement abutments on each side of the river, where the depth and swiftness of the water were less than in midstream, leaving a 90-foot gap through which the river raced with almost irresistible energy. Taking innumerable soundings of the bottom across this gap, the engineers next made a model of the river-bottom; and they built, at the edge of the gap, an upright concrete slab, 90 feet high, standing on one end and fashioned to fit all the ridges and hollows of the bottom, across the gap. This up-ended dam was held in position by cement blocks which, when all was ready, were knocked out by explosives; and,

41

as the supports went from under, the structure toppled, completely closing the gap. For a moment or two, the engineers doubtless held their breath, but the dam held; the waters of the mighty Saguenay were halted and forced to flow down the new channel to the penstocks leading to the turbines in the powerhouse. Canadian engineers had scored another triumph in their attempt to bring the great gifts of the Canadian Shield to the people of Canada.

Not only is aluminum made on the Saguenay, but mills convert timber brought from the upper waters of the river into pulp and paper, and others convert wood into various different products. The Aluminum Company of Canada built the model town of Arvida, now a city of over 10,000 people, most of whom work in the aluminum plant. They live amidst healthful and pleasant surroundings, with schools, a fine library, and a beautiful recreation centre. Although built by the company, the city is run by the people who live there; mayor and councillors are elected, as in any other community.

When the second world war came on, the need for aluminum was greatly increased and the great Shipshaw development was brought to completion by the construction of the No. 2 plant to bring the power-potential of the Saguenay to a total of 2,000,000 horsepower. For this it was necessary to dig a canal a mile and a half long through the Shield's hard rocks, and divert the course of the river in order to capture every ounce of energy. What would normally have taken five years was finished in 30 months, another engineering record in a valley that already had its share of records. The cost, of course, was tremendous, but war was the justification. At any rate, the power development is there for generations to come; and, provided world markets can be established and maintained, even at its excessive cost, it represents a greater return than many other wartime undertakings.

One of the principal sources of the Saguenay is the Peribonka River, a chief tributary of which is the Manouan River,

rising in a sprawling Shield lake about 150 miles north of
Lake St. John. In order to store water, it was decided to
dam the outlet of Manouan Lake. Everything that went
into the dam, except the stone for concrete, was flown in,
including the food and supplies needed for the army of men
employed on construction. Another dam creating an artificial lake 80 miles long was built at Passe Dangereuse, on
the Peribonka River itself; but here 143 miles of road was
built and kept open during all sorts of weather till the dam
was completed. These two dams control the water reaching
Lake St. John by way of the Peribonka, and make possible
the steady operation of the giant turbines in the plants
below.

The Ottawa River is in many respects one of Canada's
most interesting and important rivers. Champlain ascended
it in 1613, and ever since it has played a large part in Canadian history. For over 200 years it was the highway down
which the fur-brigades descended with their precious cargoes, and up which the equally heavily-laden canoes toiled
with packages of trade-goods for the interior posts. Until
the railways were built, it was an important link in the route
to the West.

For 350 miles, it constitutes the boundary between Ontario
and Quebec, but above that it is entirely a Quebec stream.
In its upper reaches, it is typical of the Shield, occupying a
shallow valley, opening into frequent lakes and lake-expansions, and dropping over many falls and rapids. At Lake
Timiskaming, really an expansion of the river, although a
considerable one, it makes an abrupt turn to the southeast
and continues in that direction to its junction with the St.
Lawrence. Below Lake Timiskaming, it flows over a series
of falls, with a total drop of 500 feet between the lake and
its mouth. Because, from the head of Lake Timiskaming to
within a few miles of its mouth, the river is interprovincial,
power sites belong equally to Quebec and Ontario and, for

this reason, power development has been slower than on a tributary such as the Gatineau, entirely within Quebec, on which a total of 529,000 horsepower has been developed.

In 1943, the Ottawa River power sites were divided by agreement between the two Provinces on the basis of which could be most effectively developed. Ontario got most of the northerly sites, while those nearer the important industrial regions of Quebec, including Carillon Rapids, with 340,000 potential horsepower, went to Quebec. So far, no development has been undertaken at Carillon, but Ontario has been quicker to take advantage of her rights on the upper river. When plants under construction are completed Ontario's installations on the Ottawa River will total over 1,000,000 horsepower.

As will be seen, most of the power that operates the pulp and paper machines in Quebec, and a great deal of the timber used in them, comes from the Canadian Shield, mostly from near its southern edge. A broad belt of territory still untouched, most of which also drains into the St. Lawrence, lies beyond this region. On the farther side of the height of land, where the rivers flow into Hudson and James Bays, or into Ungava Bay, the virgin forest still stands without an axe-mark or a saw-cut, prey only to forest fires and the ubiquitous insect or other pest. This timber must wait until shipping along the east shore of Hudson Bay is provided, and this depends upon the larger problem of navigation in Hudson Bay generally.

Enough has been shown to suggest the possibilities of this vast region. Undoubtedly, the minerals within its rocks will provide its greatest source of wealth, followed by wood products of various sorts, and its towns will be representative of these activities. The next half-century should see the rise of many new towns in this now empty land.

5

Eastern Exit to the Sea

THE Great Lakes-St. Lawrence Waterway has no counterpart anywhere in the world; nowhere else is it possible by means of a few easily constructed canals to bring ocean vessels into the heart of a continent, 2,200 miles from the open ocean. It is true that, owing to the shortsightedness of some people in Canada and the United States, who have prevented the deepening of canals on the final section of the St. Lawrence, such ocean-going vessels are limited to those drawing fourteen feet of water or less. Canadian opposition is now relatively negligible, while the need for iron ore from Labrador and New Quebec will probably convert enough of the United States opposition to enable the necessary improvements to be undertaken without much more delay.

The Canadian Shield is intimately connected with the Great Lakes, on which its southern edge rests. Lake Superior lies almost wholly within a basin scooped out of Precambrian rocks which, in the small portion south of the boundary, have produced the Mesabi Iron Range in Minnesota and the copper region of Michigan. The Canadian portion of Lake Huron, too, lies largely in a Precambrian basin, as anyone may gather who has ever seen its famed 30,000 islands of Georgian Bay. Glacial action, however, has obliterated all evidence of the underlying Precambrian rocks so far as Lakes Erie and Ontario are concerned; but at the Thousand Islands the Canadian Shield re-asserts itself, resulting in those beautiful islands. These do not offer any great impediment to navigation, but merely add to the enjoyment of the traveller;

45

farther east, in the stretch from near Prescott to Montreal, serious obstacles to navigation do occur.

The 183 miles between Lake Ontario and Montreal can be divided into five sections: (1) the Thousand Islands section, 68 miles in length, from Lake Ontario to Chimney Point, three miles below Prescott; (2) the International Rapids section, 48 miles of rapids and swift water between Chimney Point and the head of Lake St. Francis; (3) Lake St. Francis, 26 miles in length; (4) the Soulanges section, 18 miles, from Lake St. Francis to Lake St. Louis; and (5) the Lachine section, 23 miles, from Lake St. Louis to Montreal. The first two sections, comprising 116 miles, form part of the International Boundary; the other three are wholly within Canada.

Between Lake Ontario and Montreal, the river falls 226 feet, most of which is in the International Rapids, Soulanges, and Lachine sections. The International Rapids section consists of a long series of rapids, including the famed Long Sault, with a total fall of 92 feet in 48 miles. This is the section that has been holding up improvement of navigation on the river, since it is necessary to have the joint action of Canada and the United States, hitherto not forthcoming. The drop in the Soulanges section is 84 feet; and in the Lachine section it is 48 feet.

From Montreal to tidewater, a 35-foot channel is now maintained. The first work on the channel—deepening it through Lake St. Peter—was begun in 1844, and has continued more or less ever since. The Great Lakes act as settling-basins, and thus the St. Lawrence carries little silt or other detritus, which means that the dredged portions rarely give much trouble. Over most of its course from Montreal to Father Point, where it enters the estuary, a distance of 340 miles, the river now provides a wide navigation channel, safe for ships of any tonnage.

The St. Lawrence River, between the town of Cardinal and the City of Montreal, is capable of producing 5,000,000 horsepower, of which less than a million has yet been gen-

Aluminum Company's Plant, Arv

erated, and this mostly in the Soulanges section by plants now chiefly under control of the Quebec Hydro-Electric Commission. Most of the power possibilities are in the Canadian sections of the river, but in the International Rapids section a total of 2,200,000 horsepower is available for equal division between Canada and the United States. Various proposals have been made since early in the present century, but the one now tentatively agreed upon calls for a dam across the river at Barnhart Island, a short distance above Cornwall, which would utilize the whole head of 92 feet. Power would be generated in two plants, one on each side of the river. The dam would flood out the rapids, and locks would be provided for shipping.

The proposal to deepen the canals on the St. Lawrence to provide a deep navigation channel from the head of the Great Lakes to Montreal has been on the agenda of both the Canadian and United States Governments for many years. In January, 1922, the International Joint Commission, consisting of three representatives appointed by each country, after an exhaustive study, unanimously recommended the proposal. Despite opposition from eastern seaboard interests, the Harding administration seemed ready to go ahead; but, in Canada, the Mackenzie King Government, just new to office, and influenced by the determined opposition of Montreal interests backed by the Quebec Government, postponed action. Later when Canada was ready, the United States was not. Boards of experts of one sort or another have been appointed from time to time, and various modifications have been suggested. Finally, in 1932, the two Governments agreed on a proposal; but the United States Senate failed to ratify the agreement. There the matter has stuck. In all fairness, it must be said that much less opposition has come recently from Canadian sources than from across the line; and it now seems likely that need for Labrador iron ore will overcome most of the latter. Unfortunately, those parts of

winigan Company's La Tuque Plant

the United States which will benefit most from Canadian iron ore are not the ones that in the past have been opposed to the waterway scheme. Since the advantage to both countries is so great, it must now be only a matter of time till this becomes sufficiently evident to outweigh such opposition as still remains.

It may be worth while to consider some of the advantages that will accrue to the people of Canada from the completion of this waterway. The price of wheat is usually set in world markets; the growers' costs are relatively constant and cannot be trimmed very much to meet a decline in prices. The amount which the grower receives is the amount that is left after all costs are paid, one of the chief of which is transportation. It is therefore evident that any saving in transportation is a direct saving to the grower. Every time grain is handled the cost is increased. Montreal is now the greatest grain-shipping seaport in the world because all grain must be transferred there from 14-foot-draft carriers to ocean-going ships. The mammoth grain-carriers which operate on the Great Lakes, and which can handle grain more cheaply than the smaller ones, are prevented by their draft from proceeding to Montreal; their loads must either be transferred to smaller vessels at some lake port, or else unloaded for transmission to market through United States ports, which requires further handling. It is estimated that completion of the Great Lakes-St. Lawrence Waterway would save Prairie grain-growers from two to six cents a bushel. This money would not remain in the growers' pockets; its effects would be felt throughout the whole economy.

We have seen that the Hollinger interests propose to spend $200 million to develop iron ore in Labrador and New Quebec with the hope of marketing 10 million tons a year, with 20 million tons a year if markets can be found. The first and most logical market outside Canada is in the Great Lakes region of the United States. This ore would go far toward rendering Canada an independent economic unit, and naturally every cent that can be cut from the costs of production and transportation is an advantage. With a 27-foot channel all the way from Seven Islands to the Great Lakes, the laid-down cost of iron ore will naturally be less than if it must all be carried westward in ships with only a 14-foot draft. The largest ore and grain boats on the lakes can carry five times as much cargo as the smaller ones, but their cost of operation is not proportionately as great.

It is obviously an advantage to have a worldwide market in which to sell, rather than a restricted one. Large quantities of pulp and paper and other forest products might find overseas markets if they could be shipped directly from Great Lakes points. This applies to everything that Canadians export, and Canada is third among the exporting nations of the world.

Export trade, however, is not the only one that might benefit. At present, Nova Scotia coal operators are unable to send their coal much farther west than Montreal; and while they will always have to meet the competition of coal from nearer United States points, it is possible that access to the Great Lakes region would at times be an advantage to them. It is also possible that Alberta oil, piped to the head of the Lakes and there transferred to tankers, could find additional markets in the Province of Quebec if transshipment were not necessary at the foot of the Lakes.

Shipbuilders on the Great Lakes have hitherto been handicapped by the shallowness of the St. Lawrence River canals; in fact, the inability to get ships out has had the effect of practically prohibiting any shipbuilding of consequence on the Lakes. With the deepening of the canals, and with steel from Canadian ores, shipbuilding should thrive there. Capable craftsmen are already available in Canada's growing cities, but many more would undoubtedly be attracted to Canada by the prospect of work in busy shipyards.

Dr. Lesslie R. Thomson, a well-known Montreal consulting engineer, has estimated that the completion of this power and navigation project could easily result in: 12,000 new factories, with 300,000 additional workers; 1,200,000 increase in population; $800 million increase in annual wages; and $2 billion additional investment in the region directly affected by the waterway. (Dr. Thomson's estimates were made in pre-war dollars). The indirect effect upon the rest of Canada cannot be so easily estimated.

Some opponents of the scheme argue that a 27-foot channel will not handle a sufficient proportion of the world's shipping to justify the cost. Since, however, nearly 70 per cent of that shipping has a draft of less than 27 feet, and no one has suggested that the *Queen Elizabeth* or the *Queen Mary* should ever have occasion to negotiate the St. Lawrence canals, this does not appear to be a valid objection. On the other hand, since the Welland Canal has a maximum capacity of 30 feet, the excess of which over 27 feet would be wasted, and since ocean ships are steadily increasing in tonnage, it might be wiser to go to 30 feet at the outset. Both the Suez and Panama canals have been deepened beyond their original depths; but, of course, both are required to accommodate warships, which happily the St. Lawrence and Great Lakes will never be expected to do.

In the discussions that have been held concerning the St. Lawrence Waterway, stress has been laid upon goods that might be shipped from Canada, but very little is said about goods that might come in. Shipowners do not like to carry cargoes only one way; in fact, they will not do so if they can help it. Canada's products for export happen to be bulky ones, such as wheat, pulp and paper, and iron ore. On the other hand, goods imported, while perhaps of equal value in dollars, do not usually occupy so much space; and this is a matter that deserves more than a little consideration. This, of course, is a feature of Canada's trade, irrespective of the route it may follow. The greater success Canada may have in the sale of its goods abroad, the greater attention it should pay to its imports. And this is but another argument in favour of the Great Lakes-St. Lawrence Waterway, since its completion will help others to sell goods in Canada.

There is still another aspect of this question. Completion of the Waterway will require joint action by the Canadian and American peoples. In past discussions, some Canadian editors, publicists, and others, have been critical of American political and diplomatic methods. It is sometimes hard for Canadians whose Governments cannot exist without the support of Parliament, to appreciate a situation in which an American Administration may sometimes enter into an agreement that the Congress may later repudiate. This sort of criticism is not heard so often since the second world war when the two countries were able to co-operate on a wide front. In fact, the entry of Newfoundland creates a situation in which a part of the territory of Canada is, for the duration of a long-term lease, under direct American jurisdiction.

By the Treaty of Washington, signed in 1871, the people of the United States were given forever the right to navigate the Canadian portion of the St. Lawrence River, and arrangements were also made for the use by Americans of certain sections of the Great Lakes system, including the Welland Canal. In 1909, another treaty provided for the joint use of boundary waters at points where reciprocal rather than individual action was deemed advisable. This is all to the good; in a world rife with restrictions of all sorts, every case of international co-operation is a gain. Not only will the Great Lakes-St. Lawrence Waterway provide opportunity for further co-operation between Canadians and Americans, but, by providing a broader avenue for world trade, it will help to create new ties between Canadians and Americans, on the one hand, and people elsewhere, on the other, whose products will then have greater access to North American markets.

6

Ontario's Debt to the Shield

WHEN the twentieth century dawned, Ontario had a population of 2,183,000, the great majority of whom lived on farms or in small towns. Although the Province then extended northward to James Bay, few in Old Ontario were interested in the vast region between the CPR mainland and the Bay, still largely the domain of the Indian and the trapper. From time to time, certain parts had been explored by members of the Geological Survey of Canada; but at that time the geologists were still generally of the opinion that Precambrian rocks did not offer a very likely field for the discovery of precious metals. It is true that immense deposits of copper-nickel ore had been discovered at Sudbury during construction of the CPR, but this does not seem to have influenced very materially the prevailing opinion concerning the unpromising nature of the Precambrian rocks.

Although the underlying rocks were not held in very high esteem, certain sections south of James Bay were reported to be well covered with soil which was said to be good farming land. In fact, a group of pioneer settlers were doing well at Haileybury and New Liskeard, on the shore of Lake Timiskaming, and were already clamouring for a highway, or, better still, a railway to enable them to market their produce.

This caused the Ontario Government, in the first year of the new century, to send ten survey parties into the North, consisting of land surveyors, geologists, and soil experts to explore the region from the Quebec boundary to Lake Nipigon. Results of these surveys exceeded even the most sanguine expectations: a belt of arable land was reported extending from Lake Timiskaming almost as far west as Lake Nipigon, and containing about 16,000,000 acres, which became known as the Clay Belt. In addition, it was found that the area contained an "almost unlimited quantity of the best spruce for the manufacture of pulp and paper." Immigrants were then flocking into Canada, most of whom went to the Prairies, but the Ontario Government now hoped to divert some of these to its new-found land of opportunity.

The first step was to provide transportation; and the following year the Legislature authorized construction of the Temiskaming and Northern Ontario Railway (now the Ontario Northland). Surveys began immediately, quickly followed by grading and track-laying. When the rails had reached a point 104 miles from North Bay, at a place since known as Cobalt, an event occurred which changed the course of history, not only for Ontario, but for the whole of Canada. Railway workers uncovered a vein of rich silver ore, and this precipitated a mining boom such as few others have equalled. Prospectors and adventurers of all kinds were attracted from everywhere; fortunes were made by those lucky enough to stake claims in the right places.

Cobalt was a "poor man's camp"; the silver veins were at the surface, in many places so rich that large capital was not needed for development. It was a carefree camp, yet with little lawlessness; and few of those, now widely scattered, who saw it in its heyday, do not occasionally look back with nostalgia to those never-to-be-forgotten Cobalt days. Some ore was richer than any ever taken from a mine; the Lawson, with its "silver sidewalk," ran 12,000 ounces to the ton, with others richer still. Up to the end of 1950, silver to the value of more than a quarter of a billion dollars had come out of Cobalt. Most of the richest veins of the old camp are now exhausted, but recent developments suggest that within a few miles of Cobalt town deposits of silver exist which may rival in volume and richness those of the days when Cobalt was at its height.

In the same year as the Cobalt strike (1903), the Government of Canada undertook, in conjunction with the Grand Trunk Railway, to build a transcontinental railway through a more northerly section of the country than that in which the CPR was built. This line, already mentioned, called, east of Winnipeg, the National Transcontinental, began at Moncton, N.B., crossed the St. Lawrence by the famous Quebec Bridge, and struck westward along a course mostly in the Canadian Shield, cutting through the heart of the Ontario Clay Belt. The Temiskaming and Northern Ontario Railway Commission decided to extend its line to a junction with the National Transcontinental at Cochrane, and eventually the decision was reached to build the T. & N.O. through to James Bay.

Cobalt, in itself, would have justified the railway; but more was yet to come. Disappointed prospectors began a systematic search for other Cobalts, at first with little success; but, in 1909, gold discoveries were made about 90 miles northwest of Cobalt that have resulted in one of the greatest mining camps in the world. Three men were prospecting southwest of what was called Porcupine Lake, where some gold had previously been found, and a considerable amount of staking had been done, when one of the prospectors named Harry Preston slipped on a steep hillside, stripping the moss from the rock, and disclosed a ledge of quartz. This ledge, which was 21 feet wide, led to a dome-shaped structure that was literally studded with gold. The claims staked by these prospectors became the famous Dome mine.

A young man named Benny Hollinger and an older man named Alex Gillies staked a number of claims west of the lake; and since they represented different grub-stakers, they tossed a coin to see how the claims should be divided. Hollinger won the toss, and selected six claims near a small lake, which became the nucleus of the great Hollinger mine.

About the same time, another prospector, named Sandy McIntyre, and his partner, staked four claims east of Benny Hollinger's location. These became the property of McIntyre Mines Limited, one of the great gold mines of the country. Benny Hollinger and Sandy McIntyre, whose names have been perpetuated by these mines, had both been grub-staked by others, and a few thousand dollars was all either received.

Huge sums of money are needed to bring large mines into production, and few prospectors have either the connections or the qualities required for the purpose. The claims staked by Benny Hollinger were acquired by Noah Timmins and associates, who already had made fortunes at Cobalt; but, even with this money, Timmins had no easy time making the Hollinger into a mine. Doubtless the mine would have been developed in any event; but its history would have been different had it not been for the dogged determination of Noah Timmins. Hollinger Consolidated Gold Mines Limited is now interested in mining enterprises in many parts of Canada as a result of the re-investment of profits from this mine. As we have seen, it is the principal in the development of iron ore in New Quebec and Labrador.

Large-scale operations such as these require qualities which the Benny Hollingers and Sandy McIntyres do not possess; yet, without the prospector who is willing to spend months and even years combing the bush for the glint that might mean fortune, many of the greatest mines might never have been discovered. The coming of the airplane and the adoption of scientific ore-finding processes may soon eliminate this picturesque frontier character; and, considering how little he often gets for his arduous toil, it is perhaps just as well.

By 1950, the zone of gold-bearing ore discovered by Hollinger, Preston, McIntyre, and fellow-prospectors, supported 15 producing mines. The camp had a payroll of about a million dollars a month, and since its inception had produced over a billion dollars. That its full extent has yet been reached, no one would be foolhardy enough to assert; and although some of the mines have reached a depth of over a mile, values continue to hold—and in some cases to improve, —which would suggest that the Porcupine camp may count on a fairly long life, even though, since mining is a wasting industry, the time must come when, as in Cobalt, its productiveness will decline.

Timmins, largest of the four towns that have grown up about the mines of Porcupine, has a population of about 30,000. Another 10,000 people live in the nearby towns of Schumacher, Porcupine, and South Porcupine. Timmins, on the east bank of the Mattagami River, is west of the Hollinger mine; Schumacher is east of the Hollinger, with the McIntyre at its back; South Porcupine is farther east, and serves the Dome mine and others such as Paymaster and Preston East Dome; while the town of Porcupine is to the northeast, surrounded by another cluster of mines. These are well-built, modern communities. Realizing the short-lived nature of mining-towns, residents were once disinclined to build permanent homes or places of business; but that time is past, and now there is little in the type of homes or business structures to suggest that the industry upon which the community is based might in some ways be considered an unstable one.

The decision to extend the T. & N.O. Railway to a junction with the National Transcontinental had been made and construction well on its way before the discovery of the Porcupine camp, which merely gave added impetus to the builders. The line to Cochrane, as surveyed, ran east of Porcupine, and consequently a branch, 31 miles long, was built from what was called Porquis Junction to Iroquois Falls, where the Abitibi Power and Paper Company Limited was establishing a pulp and paper plant which now has a daily capacity of 675 tons of newsprint.

In their search for new mines, prospectors also ranged the country east of the railway, and as early as 1906 some gold was discovered at a number of places; but it was not till 1912 that ore as rich as that at Porcupine was struck on the shore of a little lake six miles east of Swastika station. The resulting camp became known as Kirkland Lake; and within the next few years seven large mines were developed in the relatively small strip of territory bordering the town that has grown up around them. Kirkland Lake, a bustling community of about 20,000 people, is not registered among Canadian cities, since it is unincorporated, and remains part of the municipality of Teck. The municipality comprises a large area of surrounding country, including the mines, whose taxes help to swell civic revenues. For those who think of mining camps as peculiarly "he-man" in character, it may come as a shock to learn that Mrs. Ann Shipley has been Reeve of the municipality for several years.

New names, such as Lake Shore, Wright-Hargreaves, Teck-Hughes, Macassa, and Sylvanite have been added to the lengthening list familiar to many Canadians. Harry Oakes, one of the stakers of Lake Shore, who, unlike most prospectors, saw his property through to the producing stage, and reaped a fortune thereby, retired to Nassau, Bahamas, and was made a baronet. His unsolved murder in 1943 created a world-wide sensation. William H. Wright, another founder of Kirkland Lake, who discovered the Wright-Hargreaves mine, held on, like his associate Harry Oakes, till fortune came. Wright's money launched George C. McCullagh, publisher of two Toronto daily newspapers, *The Globe and Mail* and *The Telegram*, on his spectacular career. While no other beneficiary of Kirkland Lake mines has attained such prominence as Oakes and Wright, money from these mines has built many sizeable fortunes in the past quarter-century.

Even before the Kirkland Lake strike, gold had been discovered at Larder Lake, farther to the eastward; but nothing much had come of it, and for many years the camp seemed destined to continue as a ghost-town. After many vicissitudes, two or three mines proved successful, followed, in 1938, by the Kerr-Addison, an amalgamation of several properties, which now has a daily milling capacity greater than any other in Canada, topping such giants as Hollinger and Lake Shore.

In Haileybury and New Liskeard, four and nine miles, respectively, north of Cobalt, lived some who had done well in Cobalt, Porcupine, and Kirkland Lake, and were willing to risk money in grubstaking prospectors, or in promoting new mines. Ed Horne was grubstaked by such a group, but for many years he could show little in return. Eventually in 1920, he staked some claims in western Quebec that became the nucleus of the great Noranda mine, one of the largest copper-gold producers in North America. Like Hollinger, Dome, McIntyre, and many others, Noranda Mines Limited has ploughed back much of its profits into new ventures, some of which we have already encountered. The model town of Noranda, in the shadow of its great smelter, is typical of the best of its kind, and in striking contrast to mining towns whose planning has been of a haphazard nature.

Eastward the search continued, with new mines adding to the increasing stream of gold, copper, lead, zinc, and other metals, and new towns springing up about them. At first, most of the capital for their development came from Toronto, —which, of course, draws from all over Canada and the United States. For that reason the head offices of many of the principal mines in western Quebec are in Toronto; and this has helped to convert that city in little more than a quarter-century from a sleepy provincial capital into one of the leading financial centres of the world. Undoubtedly, the building of the T. & N. O. Railway had much to do with linking this mining development to Toronto. After the discovery of Kirkland Lake, the T. & N. O. Railway Commission bought the Nipissing Central Railway, which operated an electric line between Cobalt and New Liskeard, and its

Federal charter permitted the Commission to build a branch to Noranda from Swastika station on the T. & N. O. mainline, which could not have been done under the T. & N. O.'s Provincial charter.

The Canadian Shield, across northern Ontario, consists of a relatively level upland averaging 1,000 feet above the sea, the surface of which is much broken by stream channels, ridges, and low hills. The height of land runs close to the Great Lakes, coming at one point to within less than 50 miles of Lake Superior; and consequently southward-flowing streams are short, while those flowing into James and Hudson Bays are much longer and larger.

The Shield is covered generally by a thick layer of soil left by the melting Ice Cap, and this supports considerable stands of timber, some of merchantable size, but most of it suitable only for pulp. Unfortunately, large areas have been burnt-over; but in the watersheds of the Abitibi, Mattagami, Missinaibi, and other rivers flowing into James Bay, considerable areas of spruce, balsam, and jack pine can still be found within reach of streams that can be used to float the timber to the mills. The Abitibi Power and Paper Company Limited has the plant at Iroquois Falls already mentioned, and a bleached pulp mill at Smooth Rock Falls, on the Mattagami; while the Spruce Falls Power and Paper Company Limited, a subsidiary of the Kimberly-Clark Corporation of Canada Limited, has a pulp and paper plant at Kapuskasing, on the CNR, 70 miles west of Cochrane, which produces 710 tons of newsprint, 350 tons of sulphite, and 32 tons of cellulose products a day.

Until recently, most of the world's asbestos has come from mines in the Eastern Townships section of Quebec, but with the completion in 1950 of the Johns-Manville Company's plant at Matheson, 20 miles south of Porquis Junction, a new industry was introduced into northern Ontario. An extensive belt of serpentine rocks west of Matheson contain deposits of chrysotile asbestos, and it is from the Company's Munro mine in this area that asbestos ore is secured for the plant.

The Canadian Shield does not, however, extend to James and Hudson Bays, but is separated from their shores by the Hudson Bay Lowland, a zone from 100 to 200 miles in width consisting of sedimentary rocks which are overlaid by a thick deposit of marine clays, topped by a sodden layer of peaty material. Where this zone meets the Canadian Shield, it is about 300 feet above sea level, sloping gradually toward the sea. The line of contact between this coastal plain and the Canadian Shield consists, in most places, of a more or less abrupt escarpment over which all the streams drop from 500 to 700 feet in a succession of rapids and waterfalls.

The Hudson Bay Lowland supports a sparse growth of stunted black spruce and tamarack of no value, even for pulpwood: spruce trees with a diameter of two inches are sometimes 150 years old.

This section may, however, contribute to the Canadian economy in other ways. Deposits of gypsum occur at many places which might provide material for a considerable industry. Another possible industry could be based on deposits of Cretaceous clays suitable for the manufacture of many different products, such as stoneware goods, various vitrified products, and fire brick. Other clay deposits, equally extensive, are suitable for retorts and crucibles, electric or sanitary porcelain, and floor and wall tiles. Some of the clays in this region are said to exceed in quality any others in Canada. When it is realized that the streams falling over the escarpment can nearly all produce power, it may be seen that important industries may some day be developed here.

Strange as it may seem, the region also has agricultural possibilities. Owing to the clay subsoil, the land does not drain beyond a short distance from the edges of the streams. Consequently, almost the whole surface is perpetually soaked with ice-cold water which, unable to drain away, is prevented from evaporating by a thick mantle of moss. Below the moss is a layer, several feet thick, of partly decomposed moss and other vegetation. Nevertheless, in places where the water has a chance to run off, trees, grasses, and other plants grow well.

The Moose, with its many tributaries, fans out across the Canadian Shield, and may some day be recognized as one of the great river systems of Canada. It drains an area of 42,100 square miles, with a wide variety of economic possibilities. The main river is formed by the junction of the Missinaibi and Mattagami, after which it receives the Abitibi, of about the same size, all with numerous tributaries. Since Moose River itself is entirely within the Hudson Bay Lowland, it has no rapids of consequence; but most of its branches drop over the escarpment and, between them, constitute one of Canada's great power resources. The principal installation so far is at Abitibi Canyon, 70 miles north of Cochrane, where about 264,000 horsepower is generated. Construction of this plant was begun by the Abitibi Company, but when financial difficulties occurred, the project was taken over by the Hydro-Electric Power Commission of Ontario. The Abitibi Company, however, has three installations on the Abitibi River above this point, with a total of 98,000 horse-power, most of which is used at its Iroquois Falls plant.

Since Ontario has no coal (except some low-grade lignite in the Hudson Bay Lowland), electrical power is doubly important; and the greater part of the water that turns the turbines of the Hydro-Electric Power Commisison's plants originates in the Canadian Shield. Most of the power of northward-flowing rivers remains to be harnessed; and when that is accomplished and applied to the natural resources of the region, new cities and towns will dot what is now largely an unbroken wilderness.

The Ontario Northland Railway, completed to James Bay in 1932, follows the northwestern bank of Moose River from about 15 miles below the Junction of the Missinaibi and Mattagami to Moosonee, on the estuary shore about 10 miles from the Bay. The Hudson's Bay Company's post of Moose Factory, established in 1671, and continuously in operation since then, is on an island a mile and a half farther seaward. Surveys indicate that a suitable harbour could be built at Moosonee without too much difficulty.

Meanwhile, what about the Clay Belt and the settlers whom the Ontario Northland Railway was originally intended to serve? The discovery of silver and gold helped to divert attention from agricultural settlement, while such settlement as did occur was slow because the land in most places is quite heavily timbered; and it is a heart-breaking undertaking for a settler to go into the bush, cut timber, build a cabin, uproot stumps, and clear a patch of ground in which to plant a crop. In the course of time, however, straggling settlements have grown up along the railway lines, where many fine farms may now be seen. Railways have made pulp and paper plants possible; and these, in some places, provide a market for settlers' timber, and also give them a chance to earn money in the intervals of farming. The Clay Belt has room still for many thousands of settlers. The Ontario Government is aware of the need for large-scale clearing and draining and for the provision of schools, roads, and other requirements; yet settlement continues to be slow.

This northern portion of Ontario has been described at length because it is a part of Canada about which so little is generally known; and also because of the important rôle it is likely to play in the future. Few Canadians know that strawberries as big as hens' eggs grow in the Clay Belt; that timothy hay reaches a height of four feet at Kapuskasing and elsewhere in that region; that heavy yields of oats are the rule; that bees produce more honey in the Clay Belt than anywhere else in Ontario, and that bee-keepers farther south often send bees to northern Ontario for the summer; that the Clay Belt is rapidly becoming famous for the quality of its

Spruce Falls Company's Plant, Kapuskasin

seed production; and that Cochrane is becoming an important shipping-point for hay, potatoes, and other farm products.

This part of the country is referred to as *northern* Ontario; and, of course, it is in the northern part of the province; but it is cut by the forty-ninth parallel, which forms the *southern* boundary of the four western provinces. That farm products do well in the Clay Belt has little to do with its latitude, but with the fertility of soil that once formed the bottom of Lake Ojibway, whose transient life ended with the retreat of the Ice Cap.

Development of the Canadian Shield section of Ontario has not been confined to parts served by the Ontario Northland Railway. In 1925, prospectors from Haileybury discovered gold at Red Lake, in the northwestern part of the Province, where several large mines have since been established. One of the largest of these is the Madsen, brought to its present stage by Joe McDonough, a prospector who is equally at home in the realms of finance and management. Until 1947, when highway connection with the outside was completed, Red Lake was entirely dependent upon air service, except for scow traffic in summer and tractor trains in winter.

The new status of the Canadian Shield is well illustrated by what is occurring in the region north of Lake Superior, once considered a wasteland barrier between eastern Canada and the West. A score of gold mines are in operation in that region, several in the vicinity of Geraldton and others near Long Lac; while, during 1950, a very promising goldfield near Sioux Lookout caused a considerable boom and the staking of the country for miles around. Perhaps of even greater significance is the discovery, also made in 1950, of extensive occurrences of zinc, lead, gold, and silver ore which, if present indications continue, may change the nature of the region, since the development of base-metal mines tends to establish large and more or less permanent communities.

63

al View, Sioux Lookout, Ont.

These base-metal occurrences were discovered about 45 miles north of Geraldton.

Sawmills, both big and small, are located at many points along the railways in the section north of Lake Superior, as elsewhere throughout the Shield; and at Terrace Bay and at Marathon, both new towns on the Lake shore, large pulp mills have recently been built.

The above are but the forerunners of developments to come; and while settlement may never be as dense in the mining regions as in the farming communities of Old Ontario, it may be seen that this northwestern part of the province is capable of maintaining a large population engaged in a variety of occupations.

The changing interests of Fort William and Port Arthur, now containing about 60,000 people between them, also illustrates what is happening in this once-barren land. In fur-trade days, Fort William was an important centre. There, at the eastern end of the Grand Portage between the St. Lawrence and Hudson Bay watersheds, traders from the far interior exchanged packages of furs for trade goods brought by their partners from Montreal. These meetings of East and West were always the occasion for a few days' carousal, after which both parties turned their canoes homeward. Even before the railway came, Winnipeg had succeeded Fort William as the furtrade centre, where the trade has since been conducted with more decorum. Fort William and Port Arthur, however, soon became the transfer-points for prairie grain, and now the giant elevators that line their waterfronts have a combined storage capacity of nearly a hundred million bushels.

Fort William and Port Arthur, both still greatly interested in the grain trade, are becoming important mining centres. The gold mines of Sioux Lookout, Geraldton, and Long Lac are tributary to them, as is the Steep Rock mine at Atikokan, 140 miles to the west. Production at Steep Rock already foreshadows the shift in Canada's economy from importer to exporter of iron ore which will be completed when shipments begin from Labrador and New Quebec.

The Steep Rock mine has an interesting history. Large deposits of high-grade hematite ore were discovered at the bottom of Steep Rock Lake by drilling through the ice in winter; and then the lake, 15 miles long and, in places, 150 feet deep, was drained. Before the lake could be drained, however, the Seine River, of which the lake was an expansion, had to be diverted, requiring several dams, and a canal cut through granite 100 feet wide, 70 feet deep, and 1,200 feet long. Further drilling has disclosed ore bodies of greater extent than previously expected, so that by the end of 1950, about 500,000,000 tons of ore was assured. Shipments of ore began in 1945, and by 1950 had reached 1,200,000 tons a year, to be stepped up to 4,000,000 tons by 1954, and eventually to 10,000,000 tons a year. Practically all the ore from Steep Rock is sold in the United States, but is also available for Canadian blast furnaces if required.

The Algoma Steel Corporation Limited, at Sault Ste Marie, has recently greatly increased production from its mines in the Michipicoten area, principally from its Helen mine, from which even greater production may be expected in future.

The Albany, 610 miles long, the largest river wholly within Ontario, although familiar to traders and trappers for nearly three centuries, is still unknown to most people in the Province; yet it drains an area of 59,800 squire miles,—larger than Prince Edward Island, New Brunswick, and Nova Scotia combined. Its upper reaches cut across a well-mineralized region which already has the Pickle Crow and Central Patricia mines, producing gold steadily since the early thirties, and with apparently a long life still ahead of them. All this time these mines have existed without highway connection, relying upon roundabout scow service in summer and occasional tractor service in winter, supplemented by all-year air service. The Albany has many large tributaries, one of which, the Ogoki, has been dammed to send part of its water to Lake Superior by way of Lake Nipigon. Thus, water that for ages has gone to James Bay now helps to augment the flow at Niagara.

Farther to the northwest are a number of other rivers flowing into James and Hudson Bays, of which the Attawapiskat, Winisk, and Severn are the largest. The Severn, still marked in places by dots on all but the most recent maps, indicates the extent to which Canada remains an unexplored country. Here we have a large river, draining many large lakes, still unknown, except by aerial photographs, even to geographers.

It should also be noted that Ontario is a maritime Province, with a coastline of 680 miles on Hudson and James Bays. The Ontario shores are mostly low-lying, with not many harbour possibilities; nevertheless, some countries would give much to have access even to so shallow an inlet as James Bay; and while the people of Ontario may not yet care to navigate these waters, the time may come when Hudson and James Bays will be looked upon as something more than useless expanses of frigid water, serving chiefly to chill the adjacent land.

7

Precambrian Bridge

IN some countries people may have less need for maps
than in others, but in Canada they are essential. Unless
one has a general idea of the shape and size of the
country, it is almost impossible to think beyond one's own
immediate neighbourhood, and, especially in Canada, it is not
easy to keep the general shape and size of the country in
mind without seeing a map fairly often. No home or office
should be without a good map of Canada.

Assuming, then, that you have such a map, run your eye
along a line beginning near the western end of Lake Superior,
northwestward through Lake of the Woods, Lake Winnipeg,
Lake Athabaska, Great Slave Lake, and Great Bear Lake to
the Arctic coast. This will roughly follow the line of contact
between the Precambian rocks of the Canadian Shield and
the softer Palaeozoic rocks which underlie the Great Plains.

The area lying to the northeastward of this imaginary line
consists of an irregular zone that is a continuation of a similar
area comprising most of northern Ontario and Quebec and
all of Labrador. It widens toward the Arctic, and is generally
from 200 to 500 miles in width, sloping toward Hudson and
James Bays, except in its northern portion, where the slope
is toward the Arctic Ocean. Like other parts of the Canadian
Shield, it is pitted with innumerable sprawling, indented
lakes of all sizes, connected by relatively short stretches of
stream flowing in tortuous, rocky channels, broken by rapids
and waterfalls. Except for much of the northeastern part,
most of this great region is forested.

This belt of territory consisting of Precambrian rocks was

once considered to set the northern limits of settlement or
development. People were inclined to rate it in accordance
with what it could produce in the way of crops; and, since
its agricultural possibilities are negligible, to think of it as a
wasteland. For this reason the vast extent of apparently
worthless country between the fertile fields of Old Ontario
and the equally fertile prairie lands was believed to present
an almost unsurmountable barrier. But the type of economy
now developing in Canada is still quite new and cannot be
gauged in terms based primarily upon agriculture. We have
already seen how the development of mineral and forest
resources has begun to transform this once "barren" region,
and the process is being continued all the way from Lake
Superior to Great Bear Lake and beyond. Far from being a
wasteland, this great region, with its lakes and rivers, and
more particularly the minerals beneath its surface, can now
be thought of as a connecting link between the more settled
regions of the East and the West.

The furtraders' canoe-route followed the edge of this
region. The traders kept to the streams and the lakes strung
along their courses, portaging from one to the other. From
Lake Superior they laboured over the portage made necessary
by the short, rapid descent of streams flowing eastward, and
soon reached waters bound by a circuitous course for Hudson
Bay through Lake Winnipeg. This took them to York Factory, near the mouth of the Nelson River, on Hudson Bay.

If, however, travellers were bound for the Mackenzie
Valley, they left Lake Winnipeg where the Saskatchewan
pours in and paddled up that river for about 150 miles, portaging then to the Churchill River. The latter flows almost
entirely within the Shield across the northern parts of Saskatchewan and Manitoba, traversing the widest section of the
Shield west of Hudson Bay. Probably more than any other,
the Churchill represents a typical Canadian Shield river.
Rising in a group of lakes near the western boundary of
Saskatchewan, its course consists of a succession of lakes and

lake-expansions joined by very short stretches of river, tumbling over successive rapids and waterfalls.

Streams flowing into the Churchill are similar in character; and some day—which may not be long delayed—the power resources of the Churchill and its tributaries will make possible a busy industrial region. Because of this, the centres of population in Manitoba and Saskatchewan will probably move steadily northward. So far, only one power site on the Churchill has been developed—that at Island Falls, where power is generated for the use of mines at Flin Flon, Sherridon, and Snow Lake, in Manitoba. Another will soon be developed on the Laurie River, a tributary, to supply power for the copper-nickel mine of the Sherritt Gordon Company at Lynn Lake.

In furtrade days, the Churchill formed an important link in the canoe-route to the Athabaska country. From the head of the Churchill in Methye Lake, a portage 13 miles long crosses the height of land to the Clearwater River, a tributary of the Athabaska. Here, where waters go their separate ways, —to the Arctic on the one hand, and to Hudson Bay, on the other,—is a famed scenic spot. It has often been described, but by none so graphically as by Alexander Mackenzie, who first traced the river named after him to its mouth:

> This precipice which rises upwards of a thousand feet above the plain beneath it, commands a most extensive, romantic and ravishing prospect. From thence the eye looks down on the course of the little river, by some called the Swan River, and by others the Clearwater and Pelican River, beautifully meandering for upwards of thirty miles. The valley which is at once refreshed and adorned by it, is three miles in breadth, and is confined by two lofty ridges of equal height, displaying a most beautiful intermixture of wood and lawn, and stretching on until the blue mist obscures the prospect. Some parts of the inclining heights are covered with stately forests, relieved by promontories of the finest verdure, where the elk and buffalo find pasture. . .

The natural outlet of the country drained by the Churchill is Hudson Bay, which will be discussed more fully in the next chapter. In the territory between the Churchill and Saskatchewan rivers is some of the most fertile land in Canada. At its western end, overlooking the Clearwater Valley, is a fine ranching country, which only awaits the nearer approach of settlement to come into its own. Farther east, especially in the vicinity of Lac La Ronge, are extensive areas of parkland which could be easily cleared. Rainfall is heavier here than on the prairies, and, with long days of sunshine in summer, an ideal condition for crops is created. Still farther east, along the Burntwood and Grass rivers in Manitoba, where the soil was laid down by ancient Lake Agassiz, is another potential agricultural region. The lands referred to here extend along the southwestern edge of the Shield, near enough, however, so that those engaged in the industries created by the water-power, minerals, and timber of the Shield could provide convenient markets for the settlers on these new lands.

In the Shield itself, minerals and timber will provide a livelihood for the greatest number of persons. In the south-eastern extremity of the section we are considering in this chapter, the Steep Rock mine, with an ultimate production of 10,000,000 tons of high-grade iron ore a year, has already been described. A short distance to the northwest, on the English River, at Manitou Falls, a power plant is projected by the Ontario Hydro-Electric Power Commission with a capacity of 40,000 horsepower, and three others on Winnipeg River, into which English River empties, with an aggregate of 205,000 horsepower. Already, plants on Winnipeg River—at Pointe du Bois, Slave Falls, Seven Sisters, Great Falls, and Pine Falls,—supply the City of Winnipeg and the surrounding country. About fifty miles north of the Winnipeg River, the Rice Lake mining region contains a number of gold mines, of which the San Antonio and Jeep mines are the chief producers.

In this region is also the pulp and paper plant of the

Manitoba Paper Company at Pine Falls, the only pulp and paper plant in Manitoba, but many other suitable sites await development in the northern part of the province. The possibility of cheap transportation by way of Hudson Bay might suggest some spot on the Hudson Bay Railway as a likely place for a pulp and paper plant.

The Nelson River, although only 400 miles in length, is one of Canada's great rivers. It drains Lake Winnipeg into Hudson Bay, and that lake receives, in addition to many others, the waters of the Saskatchewan, draining the greater part of the Prairies and reaching into the Rocky Mountains, and Red River, coming from the south, with which is mingled the waters of the Assiniboine and its tributaries.

The Nelson River is important in other ways. Its course lies through a highly-mineralized section of the Shield, and it is capable of producing a total of 2,000,000 horse-power, if and when its falls and rapids are harnessed. It is also worthy of note that, with the exception of the Churchill, the Nelson is the only river that entirely crosscuts the Shield. All others, from Labrador to the Mackenzie Valley, after rising in the Shield, flow away from it, toward the Arctic, Hudson and James Bays, or the St. Lawrence and Atlantic.

Until it reaches the Hudson Bay Lowland, which, like the Prairies, is underlain by Palaeozoic rocks, the Nelson flows through Precambrian country. Lake Winnipeg lies along the contact between the Shield and the Palaeozoic rocks to the west, with its eastern shore consisting of Precambrian formation and its western shore consisting of the softer rocks. As the Ice Cap retreated, waters impounded by the southern edge of the ice formed Lake Agassiz, which eventually drained away through the low gap that is now the channel of the Nelson. The Nelson River played an important part in those times, but its place in the events of the future may be even greater.

While the possibilities of mineral development along the Nelson River are still to be determined, some idea of what may be expected in that region can be gained by what is already occuring a short distance—as distances in that country are measured,—to the northwestward. In 1915, an extensive deposit of copper sulphides was discovered at a place later called Flin Flon, astride the Manitoba-Saskatchewan boundary. This deposit was discovered by a group of prospectors headed by Tom Creighton and grubstaked by a Toronto syndicate organized by John E. Hammell, who was already becoming well-known in mining circles. The history of the mine that grew out of this discovery illustrates some of the difficulties that the promoter often has to overcome. Hammell happened to be in northwestern Manitoba when he received word, and immediately went to the scene of the strike. What he saw convinced him that the strike was really important, but that the investment of many millions might be required before any return could be expected. The nearest railway point was 75 miles away, and therefore a road and eventually a railway would be needed, in addition to plants for the mining and concentration of the ore.

Hammell went immediately to New York, and in a short time succeeded in inducing the firm of Hayden Stone & Co. to take an option on the property and begin development. Drilling disclosed the existence of a large ore-body, containing gold, copper, silver, zinc, and several other valuable minerals in varying amounts, but the ore was such that no method was known by which the different metals could be profitably extracted. So, Hayden Stone dropped the project, and Hammell set about finding someone to take their place. His next group, composed of Toronto and New York interests, spent considerable sums on additional development work, but they, too, finally gave up. Then it was that Hammell succeeded in interesting the Whitneys of New York, whose metallurgists had evolved a process for the treatment of ore similar to that at Flin Flon. Before this deal was concluded, however, ten years had passed. The Whitneys incorporated the Hudson Bay Mining and Smelting Company Limited under which to operate the mine, and proceeded to invest upward of $25,000,000. In the interval, it has developed into one of the leading base-metal mines of Canada.

The Canadian National Railways built a branch line 92 miles northwestward from The Pas, on the Saskatchewan River. The company built a smelter for the production of blister copper which is shipped by rail to the refinery of Canadian Copper Refiners Limited at Montreal East, in addition to plants producing zinc and metallic cadmium at the minesite. The power plant at Island Falls, on the Churchill River, operated by a fully-owned subsidiary, generates 110,000 horsepower, which is brought to Flin Flon over a 59-mile transmission line.

In the meantime, other gold-copper deposits were discovered near Kississing Lake, about 40 miles northeast of Flin Flon. This property changed hands a number of times before much development was undertaken, and eventually was optioned by Robert J. Jowsey, of Toronto, a prospector and mine operator since Cobalt days, and Thayer Lindsley, since well-known as president of Ventures Limited, which has interests in mining enterprises all over Canada. Jowsey undertook to build about 100 miles of road and freight in the 2300 tons of heavy equipment necessary to get mining operations started. The mine became the Sheritt Gordon, and the town it created is known as Sherridon. The Flin Flon branch of the Canadian National Railways was extended 42 miles from Cranberry Portage, making possible the shipment of concentrates to the Flin Flon smelter.

During 1950, ore reserves at Sheritt Gordon were practically exhausted and mining there was being discontinued. Fortunately, however, some time previously, an immense nickel-copper deposit, said to rival that at Sudbury, had been located at Lynn Lake, 120 miles due north of Sherridon, which the Sherritt Gordon company is now developing. Almost the entire town of Sherridon, as well as the mining plant and concentrator, is being transported to the new site, the first buildings of which were moved by caterpillar tractor and sled during the winter of 1949-50. The skill with which these "cat skinners" operate is illustrated by the fact that of the first houses moved, one finished in stucco, arrived without a crack and with its chimney standing, a remarkable feat considering that the course was entirely across the rugged Precambrian countryside. Eventually, of course, a further extension of the railway will be required to enable the shipment of concentrates to the smelter, which is to be located in Alberta, where natural gas provides relatively cheap fuel.

East of Flin Flon and Sherridon, gold mines have been discovered at Wekusko (Herb) Lake, Snow Lake, and other points in a considerable area of promising territory. The mine at Snow Lake, operated by Howe Sound Exploration Company Limited, has a plant of 2,000-tons capacity. It seems probable that the territory between the Nelson and Churchill rivers—and even beyond—is destined to develop into a highly productive region. This area is within easy reach of tidewater at Churchill, and many empires of the past have subsisted on far less than this region has to offer.

Across Saskatchewan, along the southwestern edge of the Shield, many promising mining areas await adequate transportation facilities. The most promising occurrences at present are at Lac La Ronge; on Fond du Lac River; and north of the eastern end of Lake Athabaska, where pitchblende deposits are being developed. One of these deposits on the north shore of Lake Athabaska is said to exceed in possibilities anything yet discovered in Canada. If the importance of uranium continues, the effect of these deposits cannot even be imagined. Several large gold mines were once in operation at Goldfields, near the recent pitchblende discoveries at Lake Athabaska, but were closed down during the war because of rising costs of operation. If the pitchblende deposits come up to expectations, transportation facilities may soon be needed that will make the reopening

74

of the gold mines possible and also revive the ghost-town of Goldfields.

Great Slave Lake seems likely to become one of the most important mining centres in Canada. Although indications of gold had previously been noticed, the first prospects were staked about 1934, along the lower reaches of the Yellowknife River, which flows into the North Arm of the Lake. Despite the distance from the nearest settled area, five mines were in operation by the time the second world war began; but with increasing wartime costs, and scarcity of labor, they were eventually shut down. All development work was not discontinued, however, and in 1944 drilling on the property of Giant Yellowknife, controlled by Frobisher Limited, a Ventures subsidiary, disclosed the presence of an orebody which, with later developments at this mine and elsewhere in the district—including pitchblende deposits about 100 miles to the east,—seems likely to establish Yellowknife as one of the world's greatest mining camps. The Yellowknife mining area has since been extended northward for more than 150 miles, with a width of from 100 to 200 miles.

To serve this activity, the town of Yellowknife has grown from a jumble of shacks huddled on a rocky promontory and on a nearby island into a well-laid-out town whose business and residential buildings would do credit to any community of its size in Canada. Its population of over 3,000, limited by available living accommodation, constitutes a cross-section of Canadian types, with perhaps a greater percentage of the hardy and adventurous than is usually found in communities more remote from the frontier.

Yellowknife is about 700 miles due north of Edmonton, and less than 300 miles south of the Arctic Circle. Daily flights from Edmonton by Canadian Pacific Airlines keep Yellowknife in touch with the rest of the country. Perishable foods and articles of small bulk or of more than usual urgency come by air. Other requirements, however, come either by water in summer or by tractor train in winter. The nearest railway point is Waterways, Alberta, where freight is transferred to river boats. Except for a 16-mile obstruction between Fitzgerald, Alberta, and Fort Smith, District of Mackenzie, where transshipment is necessary, water-transport to Yellowknife is uninterrupted.

In winter, freight comes by way of Grimshaw, on the Northern Alberta Railways. From this point, a highway extends northeasterly 400 miles to Hay River settlement, near the western end of Great Slave Lake. It is now an all-weather road over which trucks are operated, but previous to its completion traffic was handled exclusively by tractor trains made up of caterpillar tractors hauling long strings of sledges. Such freight as comes over this route in summer is transferred to barges at Hay River and continues by water to Yellowknife; but in winter tractor trains are still used to cross the lake-ice.

During their short history, despite the difficulties, great quantities of freight of all sorts have passed over these two routes to Yellowknife. Some idea of what this amounts to may be gained when it is realized how much heavy machinery and other equipment has been required to bring about the remarkable transformation that has occurred there in the past few years. It is only a matter of time, of course, till railway connection will be imperative.

On the south shore of Great Slave Lake, at Pine Point, and also on the north shore, extensive lead-zinc occurrences have been found. As far back as 1929, Robert J. Jowsey prospected and staked claims at Pine Point, but he was ahead of his time. More recently, a concession has been given by the Government of Canada to Consolidated Mining and Smelting Company of Canada Limited and Ventures Limited conferring on them the exclusive exploration rights on an area aggregating 500 square miles in the Pine Point region. Prospects so far are said to be very favourable, and it is likely that a smelter will eventually be built, as well as a railway to connect with the Northern Alberta Railways. If and when such a railway is built, extension to serve Yellowknife should not be a difficult matter.

Streams flowing into Great Slave Lake are capable of producing ample power for any possible requirements. The Lockhart River, which drains a series of lakes east of Great Slave Lake, is one of the most important. It rises in Mackay Lake, which is about 60 miles long and 1,415 feet above sea-level. In the 30 miles between Mackay and Aylmer lakes, the river drops 185 feet. Aylmer Lake discharges into Clinton-Colden Lake with a drop of only four feet, and the drop is also slight between Clinton-Colden and Ptarmigan lakes, but in the 15 miles between the latter and Artillery Lake, there is a further drop of 32 feet, while in the 25 miles between Artillery Lake and Great Slave Lake, the drop is 695 feet.

Other power is available on Slave River, which drops 125 feet in 16 miles, on the Taltson and Snowdrift rivers, both of which flow into Great Slave Lake between the mouth of Slave River and the eastern end of the Lake, and on Hay River, at the western end of the Lake, about 40 miles above its mouth where there are two falls of 140 and 52 feet, respectively. The town of Yellowknife and nearby mines are at present supplied with power from two plants, one on the Yellowknife River not far above its mouth, and the other, more recently built, on Snare River, about 90 miles north of the town.

When the gold mining region to the north of Great Slave Lake and the base-metal deposits on the south are developed, with other mineral resources which a railway and smelter will make available, the region should become a most important one, the extent of which can now only be surmised. As with other regions, the rôle of a prophet is a thankless one; yet men of experience, not entirely given to wishful thinking, can be found who agree that in time this region will become one of the most important in Canada. And when it is realized that Yellowknife is 1,000 miles in a direct line north of the International Boundary, it will be seen that at last Canada may attain breadth as well as length.

The eastern end of Great Slave Lake is within the Canadian Shield, which, though productive of some timber, is entirely without agricultural possibilities. Its western end, however, lies above softer Palaeozoic strata and is flanked by a number of areas of arable land, principally along the valley of Hay River. With the growth of population in the Great Slave Lake area, a considerable farming community can ultimately be expected in this section, for which the mining regions should provide markets.

This is by no means the most northerly point of possible settlement. Three hundred miles farther north, on Great Bear Lake, is the present source of radium and uranium, which may yet revolutionize our way of life. In 1929, Gilbert LaBine, who had been an Ontario prospector since the Cobalt days, and had subsequently extended his search into Manitoba, decided to try his luck in the region of Great Bear Lake. He chartered a plane at Edmonton and flew in for a quick look over the country; and while on the outward flight noticed geological formations near the southeastern angle of the Lake that interested him sufficiently to lure him back the following spring. Early in May, he was again at Great Bear Lake and shortly after his arrival discovered two small veins containing stringers of silver in a matrix of black rock which was later identified as pitchblende.

The story of the development of a mine almost on the Arctic Circle, when all ore must be transported 1,300 miles upstream, and transshipped twice at portages, followed by 2,000 miles by rail to the refinery at Port Hope, Ontario, is one of the most thrilling stories in all the thrilling history of Canadian mining. The production of radium from the Eldorado mine broke the monopoly price previously maintained by the European cartel with sources of supply in the Belgian Congo, and the price dropped from $50,000 to

$25,000 a gram. An entirely unexpected adjunct of the product of the Eldorado mine is atomic energy with its infinite possibilities for both good and evil. So vital were these possibilities that in 1944 the Government of Canada expropriated the mine and everything connected with it and has since operated it as a public enterprise.

These, then, are some of the possibilities inherent in the Canadian Shield which cuts across the heart of Canada. Settled areas on the Plains, in Alberta and Saskatchewan, are in general too far from the Shield to benefit much from its power resources; but in Manitoba integration of Shield and Prairie has already begun. Winnipeg, once the fur-traders' capital, became one of the world's great wheat centres after the railways came, and will doubtless continue so; but more and more it is becoming an important mining centre, although that phase is still in its infancy. As already intimated, prophesy in connection with Canada's future (in a regional way) is full of risk, as many examples will testify. Nevertheless, one might be tempted to nominate The Pas as the eventual runner-up to Winnipeg in Manitoba. At present, it is a small community on the south bank of the Saskatchewan River, the western terminus of the Hudson Bay Railway. It, however, is within 500 miles of tidewater; it has at its back the Flin Flon mine and the Lynn Lake development to come, and many others in embryo in the territory adjacent. Tributary to The Pas are extensive timbered areas, which could easily make it a centre for pulp and paper, as it already is to a limited extent for lumber. Good farming land is available in the vicinity, especially in the Carrot River Valley to the southwest. With ample power that can be derived from the Nelson River as well as from the Saskatchewan, the prediction that an important industrial region might develop there should not involve too great a risk. One of the factors upon which such an estimate is made involves the practicability of the Hudson Bay route, which will be considered in the next chapter.

79

View, Yellowknife, N.W.T.

8

Ocean Path to the Prairies

FOR two hundred years Hudson Bay was the port of
entry for what later became the Canadian Northwest;
year after year the little sailing ships of the Hudson's
Bay Company unloaded their trade goods and supplies at
Churchill harbour and took on board cargoes of pelts in return. Without sailing aids of any sort, without buoys or lights,
and without information concerning ice movements or what
the weather held in store for them, skippers of these little
ships established a record for safe and regular navigation
unsurpassed anywhere else in the world.

Western Canada's first settlers, and the first livestock to
reach the Plains, also came by way of Hudson Bay. In the
summer of 1811, a shipload of Highlanders sent out from
Scotland by the Earl of Selkirk to settle in the Red River
Valley arrived at York Factory, at the mouth of the Hayes
River, on Hudson Bay. They arrived too late in the season
to continue the journey to their destination, and wintered on
Hudson Bay. Next year, however, after building boats, they
travelled up the Hayes and Nelson rivers to Lake Winnipeg,
and up the lake to its head, where Red River enters from the
south. Ascending the river to its junction with the Assiniboine, where the city of Winnipeg now stands, they built
their huts and for the first time broke the prairie sod over
which for ages the bison had roamed. Following these, other
groups of settlers came by the same route; in fact, it was the
easiest and most natural way to reach the western plains.

Hudson Bay is really an inland sea, 900 miles long by
from 300 to 520 miles wide, extending far into the heart of

Canada, and is entered from the Atlantic by Hudson Strait, 450 miles long by from 37 miles at its narrowest to 120 miles at its widest. Tides, which reach heights of from 30 to 40 feet in the inlets, and from 12 to 15 feet in the Strait, keep the latter from freezing over. The ice that collects in the Strait at certain times of the year comes chiefly from farther north; and now that airplane reconnaissance and radio communication can be provided, navigational hazards from ice in the Strait can be greatly reduced, if not eliminated entirely.

At one time it was believed that Hudson Bay itself did not freeze over, but recent aerial investigation has established the fact that the Bay usually freezes about the middle of January. Experience elsewhere—in the Gulf of Finland, for example,—suggests that when sufficient traffic is available to justify the necessary navigational aids, freezing over of the Bay need not seriously interfere with navigation.

Although, after the failure of the Red River settlement, no other settlers came through Hudson Bay, the Hudson's Bay Company continued to receive its supplies as in the past; but when railways linked the Atlantic and the Pacific, the route fell into disuse. Later, when Prairie grain-growers, attempting by every means in their power to lower the cost of marketing their grain, considered the nearness of tidewater at Hudson Bay as compared with the distance to Montreal and the Atlantic ports, they began an agitation for a railway to Hudson Bay which did not end till the railway was built.

Following is a table showing distances between important Prairie points and Liverpool *via* Hudson Bay, as compared with the distances from the same points by way of the Great Lakes:

	Via Great Lakes Miles	Via Churchill Miles
Winnipeg	4,393	3,919
Portage la Prairie	4,449	3,864
Brandon	4,527	3,863

Regina	4,750	3,769
Moose Jaw	4,792	3,812
Saskatoon	4,878	3,773
Calgary	5,226	4,172
Edmonton	5,224	4,072

The building of the Panama Canal provided an alternative outlet for Alberta points, and thereafter less was heard from farmers in that province concerning the Hudson Bay route, while many Manitoba people lost some of their earlier enthusiasm when freight rates to the East were lowered somewhat; and certain Winnipeg interests became more than lukewarm when it appeared that the Hudson Bay route might divert some traffic from Winnipeg. For these reasons, the most consistent advocates of the route are in Saskatchewan. At one time the "On to the Bay Association" (now the Hudson Bay Route Association) had its head office in Winnipeg; but with the lessening of interest in Manitoba, the office was moved to Regina. It is perhaps significant that Regina is 134 miles (by rail) nearer Churchill than is Winnipeg.

Before the lands farther west were settled, however, Manitoba farmers had begun their agitation. At that time the Province, in its original size and shape, seemed like a postage stamp on the map, surrounded by the vast extent of the federally-administered Northwest Territories. This meant that the greater part of any railway destined for Hudson Bay would lie beyond the borders of the Province, and should more properly be built under Federal auspices. Nevertheless, many railway promoters were attracted to the idea of a railway to Hudson Bay, lured more particularly by the prospect of land subsidies offered by the Federal Government of 6,400 acres per mile for lines in Manitoba and 12,800 acres per mile in the Northwest Territories.

Many charters were granted, but few resulted in any railway mileage. One company which received its charter as early as 1880, actually built a line 40 miles north from Winnipeg; then the company failed and eventually its tracks were torn up. Meanwhile, other lines were extending north-westerly from Winnipeg, and, although the wheat lands of Saskatchewan, rather than Hudson Bay, was their destination, this brought them somewhat nearer the Bay.

Finally, in 1905, the firm of Mackenzie & Mann, railway contractors who had built and controlled the Canadian Northern Railway, with assistance from the Federal Government, began construction of a branch from Hudson Bay Junction, on the CNR Winnipeg-Prince Albert line, to The Pas, a distance of 88 miles. This, at any rate, was heading in the right direction, and brought the end of steel to within little more than 400 miles of the Bay.

Prairie hopes were high in 1908 when the Federal Government, withdrawing land subsidy offers, announced its intention to build a railway from The Pas to Hudson Bay as a national undertaking, the cost to be financed from the sale of Prairie homestead and pre-emption lands. Before construction was begun, however, the Government appointed John Armstrong, C.E., as chief engineer, with instructions to make a complete investigation of the project and report his recommendations concerning type of construction, which terminal—Churchill or Port Nelson—he favored, and all other pertinent matters. Armstrong reported in the fall of 1909, endorsing the project in general, and, much to the surprise of many advocates of the railway, recommended Port Nelson, rather than Churchill, which had been the Hudson's Bay Company's chief port of entry for over 200 years.

Mr. Armstrong gave comparative estimates for a line to Port Nelson and one to Churchill. Taking the Churchill route first, he stated that the initial section of approximately 120 miles from The Pas would be through comparatively level or smooth country, affording easy grades and cheap construction. Seventy per cent of the grading would be in clay loam and thirty per cent in sand, gravel, swamp or muskeg. He explained, however, that what was called muskeg in that region might more correctly be defined as swamp, since good bottom could usually be found at a depth of three or four feet, seldom exceeding seven or eight. The second section of 120 miles would be through a granite country, where rock cutting would be necessary, otherwise railway construction would present no problems. The roughest country would be in the third section, also consisting of 120 miles, where the line would cross the divide between the Nelson and Churchill watersheds, but the summit was quite low. The fourth section, from Mile 360 to Churchill, a distance of 150 miles, would not require much excavation, but the final 70 miles over the tundra might, he thought, present some difficulties because of the perpetually frozen subsoil. Maximum grades of 0.4 northbound, and 0.6, southbound, could be secured for the whole line.

With respect to the Port Nelson route, the Chief Engineer reported that the type of country through which the line would run was practically the same as that which the Churchill line would traverse in its first section, with little rock, much clay loam, and small percentages of sand, gravel, and swamp, and no tundra. Total distance from The Pas to Port Nelson would be 424 miles, only 22 miles longer than an air line, which would probably result in the most direct line of railway of its length in America. The report contained detailed cost estimates. The total for the Churchill route, including construction with 80-pound rail; station and other necessary building construction; terminal facilities and two 4,000,000-bushel elevators, was set at approximately $25,-000,000; while the estimate for similar type of construction and facilities on the Port Nelson line was around $21,000,000.

Although the decision in favor of Port Nelson was made largely on the basis of lower construction costs, the question of the suitability of the respective ports was also taken into consideration. Mr. Armstrong seemed to think that the possibilities of establishing a satisfactory harbor at Churchill were less favorable than at Port Nelson, and he undoubtedly underestimated most of the difficulties that would be encountered at Nelson. Perhaps the deciding factor was that, relatively speaking, the climate at Nelson is a more temperate one; while Churchill, with its perpetually frozen subsoil (called permafrost), is definitely in the subarctic regions, and presented problems with which he as an engineer was probably unfamiliar. For this reason he may have approached his task with a prejudice against Churchill and a preference for Nelson with its more normal (for him) conditions.

The Government decided not to make an immediate choice of the terminus, but to proceed with the project since for the greater part of the distance both routes would be the same. Accordingly, amidst much rejoicing on the Prairies, the first sod was turned at The Pas on September 28, 1910, by Hon. George P. Graham, Minister of Railways, and work was almost immediately begun on the bridge across the Saskatchewan at The Pas; and the following spring a contract was let for the grading of the first section—to Thicket Portage, 185 miles. In 1911, the Laurier Government was defeated on the question of reciprocity with the United States, and a new Government took office at Ottawa. The change did not materially affect the fortunes of the Hudson Bay Railway, since, as the new Premier, Mr. (later Sir) Robert Borden said, the Conservative Party had been pledged to the building of the railway since 1895, but some time was required for the new Minister of Railways to get his bearings.

In the spring of 1912, however, a contract was let for the grading of the second section,—from Thicket Portage to Split Lake, 68 miles; and in the following September the Minister announced the letting of the contract for the third and last lap, declaring that the road would be completed in 1914. During 1912, the Government had come to the decision to adopt Port Nelson as the terminus. The bridge across the Saskatchewan River, 850 feet long, was completed by the end of 1912; work on the grade had been continuing and some track had been laid; nevertheless it was evident that the Minister's promise of completion by 1914 could not be fulfilled. It was therefore not till some time in 1915 that the grade reached Mile 332, with steel laid as far as the rock cut at Manitou Rapids,—Mile 241. Crossing Armstrong Lake, at Mile 226, had presented unexpected problems, principally because the bottom was of soft mud. The difficulty was finally overcome by building cribs of timber which were filled with rock and allowed to sink into the ooze until they became stable. Then bridge stringers were laid from crib to crib to support the tracks. Across this structure the 1,000 tons of steel for the Manitou Rapids bridge over the Nelson River was safely transported, and the bridge, 612 feet long, with a main span of 304 feet, was ready for traffic in April, 1916. There had been some talk of completion by 1916, but the country was at war and many other problems confronted the Government.

Then, in 1917, a new Government took office,—the Union Government, dedicated to the task of winning the war. Composed of representatives of the two principal parties, it did not feel the need, as a purely party government might have done, for placating various sections of local opinion. Consequently, despite continued agitation by Prairie people, interest in the Hudson Bay Railway lagged considerably at the governmental level; and in 1918, although the grade had been completed to Port Nelson and track laid on all but 92 miles, work was suspended entirely. A second crossing of the Nelson had been made at Kettle Rapids, with a bridge 1,000 feet long, having two 300-foot spans and a central one of 400 feet. Total expenditure had been $13,500,000 for the road, and $6,000,000 for harbour improvements at Port Nelson. Arrangements were made with the CNR to operate a limited service to Pikwitonei—Mile 214,—to serve the settlements that had sprung up in anticipation of the railway.

Enthusiasm for the Hudson Bay Railway has never been very keen in the East, where Canadian public opinion is largely formed and controlled. Canadian railways, interested in the long haul, were definitely opposed to it; many large fianancial concerns centred largely in Toronto and Montreal, were also generally opposed, and with them went most eastern newspapers and other publications. In 1920, a special Committee of the Senate of Canada investigated the navigational possibilities of Hudson Bay and Strait, about which there was considerable difference of opinion. After hearing evidence from all whose opinions seemed to have a bearing on the subject, the Committee reported that the route was feasible, both from the standpoint of navigation, and ultimately of economical operation; that the minimum shipping season was four months; that Nelson was superior to Churchill as a port; that the fishery resources of Hudson Bay were extensive (not borne out by later experience); and that the region was rich in potential mineral resources.

In 1921, another new Government—that of Mr. Mackenzie King,—took office at Ottawa; and at first it seemed less favourable to the Hudson Bay Railway than any of its predecessors. Despite the recent findings of the Senate Committee, the new Minister of Railways, in 1922, gave instructions that the rails should be torn up; but such a storm of protest arose from the sorely-tried Prairie community that the order was quickly rescinded. Nevertheless, although the rails remained, the forest was allowed to invade the right of way; the neglected track twisted and rusted; bridges and culverts were washed away; in some places the embankment completely disappeared; and for long stretches the line was impassable.

Prairie people, who for so many years had seen their hopes repeatedly deferred, although greatly disappointed, were not discouraged. They at length succeeded in persuading the Government that the project should be proceeded with; but, still complicating the issue, was the old controversy as to whether Port Nelson or Churchill was the better terminus; and this, before doing anything else, the Government now decided to settle. The eminent British port authority, Dr. (afterwards Sir) Frederick Palmer, was engaged to make an examination of the whole subject; and in 1927 he definitely recommended the abandonment of Port Nelson and the substitution of Churchill.

Dr. Palmer's principal reasons were three: (1) a better harbour could be made at Churchill than at Port Nelson, since any harbour that could be constructed at the latter port would not admit ships of more than 26 feet draft, and then only at high tide; whereas, at Churchill, ships drawing up to 30 feet of water could enter at any stage of tide; (2) cost of completion at Churchill would be less than that required to finish the port at Nelson; and (3) the time required would be three years less at Churchill than at Nelson.

In view of this, it is difficult to understand why the decision should ever have been made to adopt Port Nelson; but, probably reputations were at stake based on opinions once given, even though evidence in support of them now seems less than sufficient. Once the decision to transfer the terminus to Churchill was made, however, construction of the railway was resumed without loss of time. The Canadian National Railways, as agents for the Department of Railways, was assigned the task, with J. G. MacLachlan as district engineer. The line to Port Nelson up to Mile 356 was continued, and from there the new line was located. By the end of 1926, the old line had been reconditioned as far as Kettle Rapids; and by April 1, 1929, steel had reached Churchill.

Building the new section was a challenge to the engineers; methods never before tried in railway construction were adopted. The engineers took advantage of factors at first thought to be adverse ones and turned them to good account. Thus it was soon recognized that instead of frozen soil being a detriment in securing a stable foundation for the roadbed, it could be used to good purpose if the ground were prevented from thawing and the natural moss insulation left undisturbed on the surface. In order to do this, it was found necessary to drain away all surface water from the right of way, and, without in any way disturbing the moss, the roadbed was built of material hauled by train. Track was therefore laid on the original surface without previous preparation. It was found that construction could be carried on much better in winter than in summer, as in winter the sloughs and soft spots were all frozen. After the track was laid, ballasting was conducted from both ends and from an intermediate point, so that by the middle of September, 1929, the line was completely ballasted and in condition to handle carefully managed traffic.

Although the settlement at Churchill, consisting chiefly of the Hudson's Bay Company's establishment, a mission, and other traders, had previously been on the western side of the Churchill River near its mouth, it was decided to lay out a new townsite, the railway terminals and yards, as well as wharves and other port facilities on the eastern side of the river. Not only was that shore more sheltered, but the cost and inconvenience of a bridge across the river were avoided. During 1930 and 1931, the deep water wharf was built, 1,856 feet long at the face by 250 feet wide over 500 feet of its length, and 300 feet wide for the remainder. The cribs supporting the wharf, most of which are 154 feet long and 49 feet wide at the base, were constructed of 12″ x 12″ Douglas fir, sunk to crib seats 32 feet beneath the low water mark.

Since the principal purpose of the Hudson Bay Railway was to move Prairie grain to market, a modern 2,500,000-bushel elevator was built, capable of being increased, if need be, to hold 10,000,000 bushels. Loaded grain cars are emptied at the elevator by four car-unloaders, each with a capacity of eight cars—about 10,000 bushels—per hour. After the grain has been elevated, it is carried to the deep water wharf by a four-belt conveyor system. The shipping gallery, 1,462 feet long, provides berths for three ships at a time. Twenty boat-spouts, about 65 feet apart, provide for a maximum discharge of four streams at the rate of 20,000 bushels per hour for each stream.

The first grain to pass through the Port of Churchill was

shipped on September 12, 1929,—before the elevator was built—and consisted of 2,000 pounds of specially selected No. 1, Northern, wheat, which was loaded on board the Hudson's Bay Company's vessel *Ungava*. Regular grain shipments began in 1931, when the *Farnsworth* and the *Warkworth* between them sailed with half a million bushels. In successive years, varying numbers of ships have cleared from Churchill, the greatest number being 15 in 1934. Following the outbreak of war, owing to lack of convoys, no shipments were made except in 1943, when eight ships loaded at Churchill for eastern United States ports. The first incoming freight arrived in 1932, when the steamer *Pennyroyal* unloaded a cargo. Lack of incoming cargoes is one of the principal drawbacks of the Hudson Bay route, and must some day be remedied.

While emphasis is placed upon the importance of the Hudson Bay Railway as an outlet for the products of the prairie region, it is possible that eventually it will also justify its existence as a means of developing the varied resources of the territory through which it runs. As we have seen, it is already doing its part to aid in the development of mines located farther north. At Wekusko, 81 miles from The Pas, tractor trains and trucks connect with a large gold mine at Snow Lake, where a new mining town has come into existence. Farther along the line, at Ilford station, regular tractor train services connect with God's Lake and Knee Lake mining areas; and as this territory becomes more thoroughly prospected, it is to be expected that other mining communities will come into existence.

The Hudson Bay Railway passes through three general geological belts, across which the rivers and the railway cut at right angles. The most southerly is a tract of about 60 miles in width consisting of flat limestone formation (Ordovician), thinly covered with, or bare of soil, drained southward to the Saskatchewan River. Next, and most important, is the Precambrian section, about 250 miles wide, where the under-

lying crystalline rocks are deeply covered by clay soils.
Between these two formations are outcrops of Huronian and
Keewatin rocks, which elsewhere are mineral-bearing, and
which here should repay intensive prospecting. Beyond the
Precambrian section, the third belt consists of limestone
formations (Ordovician overlain in places by Silurian) with
a wet clay and gravel subsoil, surfaced with mosses and
frozen bog. This section lies within the Hudson Bay Lowland.

Much of the area is timbered; and while not a great deal
of merchantable timber exists, the amount available for pulp
is considerable. As already suggested, pulp and paper plants
are indicated at The Pas, and probably at other points along
the railway.

Agricultural possibilities also exist. As previously mentioned, part of this area was once covered by the waters of
Lake Agassiz, in which were laid down the soils which make
Manitoba famous and which extend into this region. It is
estimated that a belt of approximately 6,400,000 acres is suitable for agriculture between the Nelson and Churchill rivers
northeast of Mile 130, 50 to 75 per cent of which is suited to
mixed farming. Areas of swamp soils could also be made
available for agriculture if properly drained.

By 1930, three trains a week—two freights and one mixed
—were being operated over the line, and service at this level
was continued until the outbreak of war, when, while grain
shipments were discontinued, much war material passed over
the line to Churchill, where an important military establishment, mainly American, was maintained. In addition to
supplies reaching Churchill by rail, considerable quantities
also arrived by water. Consequently, in 1942, both the Port
of Churchill and the railway, for the first time, showed an
operating surplus, the former of $7,668.74, and the latter of
$112,120.75. Since the end of the war, traffic between The
Pas and Churchill has reverted to its pre-war status.

The Hudson Bay Railway is typical of other projects across

Canada whose potential value to the national economy is far greater than that which accrues to it as a local enterprise. In this categary may also be placed the industrialization of the Maritimes and the completion of the Great Lakes-St. Lawrence Waterway.

The Hudson Bay Railway is entirely within the territory of the Province of Manitoba, as is the port of Churchill. The Manitoba Government can devote to this region only the amount of attention and money that its limited population appears to justify; but, without the general development of the country through which it runs, the railway—a federal project,—cannot hope to succeed. The same thing happened in connection with the National Transcontinental and Grand Trunk Pacific, as has also been the case with the Trans-Canada Highway.

9

All This And Oil, Too

U NTIL quite recently, the two resources needed most by Canada in order to become a great industrial nation were oil and iron. Now she is on her way to becoming a first-rank producer of both. It is hard to say whether the iron ore of Labrador, New Quebec, or northwestern Ontario or the petroleum of the western plains is the more valuable. Probably the verdict should go to oil, which not only provides power, but also the raw materials for many hundreds of products. In addition to the oil, the plains region produces billions of cubic feet of natural gas, providing both power and raw materials.

The western oil and gas region consists of a broad geosyncline lying east of the Rocky Mountains, extending from south of the American border to the Arctic Ocean, a great part of which shows evidences of favourable oil or gas structure. Some geologists believe that when this field is finally determined it will prove to be one of the four greatest areas of oil concentration in the world, with a chance of being the greatest.

Perhaps it will be well at this point to consider how it is that geologists can indicate that one section of the earth's crust may be favourable for the accumulation of oil, while no such possibility exists in another area. In order to understand why the plains region is a likely place to look for oil, it will be necessary to go back many millions of years and consider how the country appeared then and at various times in the interval. During hundreds of millions of years, while high mountains towered above what is now the Canadian Shield, the area west of the margin marked by the line of lakes referred to in an earlier chapter lay under the sea. Slowly, layers of ooze hundreds of feet thick accumulated on the bottom, consisting chiefly of the bodies of marine organisms of all descriptions. During further ages, as the granitic mountains to the east were worn down by water, frost, and even by wind, materials carried by streams also spread over the floor of this great western sea. In time the ooze became limestone, while materials from the land hardened into sandstones, shales, and other types of sedimentary rocks. These deposits became thicker and thicker; and as their thickness increased, they sagged under their own weight, forming a deep trench running northwest and southeast.

Then, as the earth's crust shrank during a period of adjustment, the mountain ranges to the west were thrust up, somewhat as wrinkles appear on the skin of a raisin or a prune. The Rocky Mountains are merely *upright* sections of what farther east are more or less horizontal layers of sedimentary rocks. As evidence of this, it is possible to find marine fossils on the mountain-tops. The mountain-building movement served to deepen the depression on the eastern flank of the mountain ranges by causing the strata to buckle downward, and into this depression silt-laden streams continued for countless ages to discharge their loads. In time, the land along the western edge of the plains, bordering on the mountains, reached elevations greater than anywhere farther east.

Limestone, as we have seen, resulted from the ooze that once collected at the bottom of the sea. The bony parts of marine organisms within the ooze became stone, while the soft parts became tiny globules of petroleum, some of which were broken down into gas. During the mountain-building era, when this region was subjected to lateral squeezing, the various strata were forced into folds, of which those curving upward are called anticlines, and those curving downward, synclines. Since limestone and sandstone are porous, the petroleum, under pressure from the gas, spread through the rock and eventually was trapped in the tops of such anticlines as were overlaid by shales (formed of clays) through which oil and gas cannot pass.

It is therefore known that wherever there are well-defined anticlines, chances exist that somewhere beneath them pools of oil may be found. In some cases—and this is particularly so along the Alberta foothills, where the structure has been badly twisted and broken,—accumulations that once existed are found to have disappeared. They may have merely migrated to other parts of the subterranean regions and may still be found, or they may have escaped to the surface.

Along the Athabaska River, about 250 miles north of Edmonton, deposits of "tar sands" indicate the existence at one time of a huge concentration of petroleum which later became exposed, possibly by the action of glacial ice. Although most of the volatile portions of these deposits have evaporated, petroleum can still be extracted from them. During the second world war, 17,000 barrels of oil were taken from 19,000 tons of these sands. The method used is not commercially profitable, but if a market were available there is little doubt that a more satisfactory one could be devised. It is estimated that the Athabaska tar sands contain from 100 to 250 billion barrels of oil, which could supply the whole world for a century on the basis of present consumption. This, at any rate, gives some indication of what may still be awaiting the drills in other parts of the great geosyncline that stretches from the International Boundary to the Arctic.

Some of the early homesteaders in southern Alberta found gas bubbling out of the water in sloughs or creeks. Drillers, taking the cue, tapped underground reservoirs of gas which was piped to heat and light the cities. Medicine Hat, Lethbridge, and Calgary were piped for gas in this way; and gas wells were found later at Viking, to supply the city of Edmonton.

W. S. Herron, a rancher living about 40 miles southwest of Calgary, showed one of these seepages to A. W. Dingman, a well-driller, who induced a group of Calgary businessmen to subscribe the money with which to drill what became known as the Dingman well. In the fall of 1913, a small quantity of oil was encountered at a relatively shallow depth, which caused a mild flurry of excitement. In the following May, however, a heavier flow was struck, and Calgary was off to a boom such as has rarely been equalled.

Following the earlier flurry, the oil rights in a considerable area radiating from the Dingman well were secured by speculators, and a number of oil companies were incorporated. Most of these companies had difficulty raising money in a community still smarting under the collapse of a real estate boom; but when the second strike occurred their offices were stormed by applicants for shares. Many company-promoters, eager to ride the golden tide, were not above selling shares in companies not yet incorporated. People queued up in front of oil-company or brokers' offices, were kept in line by mounted policemen. Vacant stores and hotel lobbies became brokerage offices overnight. Clerks worked at top speed writing receipts for money literally forced on them by frantic speculators; wire waste-baskets filled with money and stock-applications were piled, from floor to ceiling, behind the counters in some of these offices.

Booms feed on sensation, but after the Dingman strike early in May, no other occurred to feed the flames. Only a few of the many companies so recently incorporated had begun drilling, and consequently no wells were within reach of possible oil-bearing formations. Then came the first world war, and with it the boom flickered out. A small number of companies continued drilling, but as the war dragged on less and less interest was taken by the general public in the possibilities of oil in what became known as Turner Valley.

After the war, interest in the oil fields revived somewhat, and the search was renewed, this time by companies with more capital at their disposal. One of these, the Royalite Oil Company, which later became a subsidiary of Imperial Oil Limited, made a sensational strike in 1924 when its well No. 4 blew in with a daily production of 700 barrels of naphtha and 21 million cubic feet of gas. Other wells had been drilled which produced naphtha, in addition to varying quanties of gas, but none to compare with Royalite's wonder well, whose blazing torch illuminated the countryside for years until the gas was put to better use.

In 1936, crude oil was struck on the western flank of the field, raising hopes that at last the great pool had been discovered, and this precipitated another speculative flurry. Despite the fact that Home Oil Company's Millardville No. 2 well, located in this section, in the 10 years of its existence, produced over 1,500,000 barrels of oil, this was not yet the main area of concentration. Turner Valley's production reached its highest in 1942, when a total of 10,000,000 barrels was produced; since then production has declined.

Although in its life of over 35 years, Turner Valley has produced about 100,000,000 barrels of oil, the greater part within the final 10 years of that period, oil men were certain that it did not contain the chief concentration of oil. Far and near, the search continued; wells were drilled within a few miles of the International Boundary; others on the Alberta-Saskatchewan border. The search extended to the Mackenzie Valley, far to the northward. Yet it is safe to say that had such a great area of promising oil territory been in almost any other country, its development would not have been so slow; for it must be admitted that, in the search for oil, as in other cases where a risk must be taken, Canadians have lacked enterprise.

Even before the first Calgary oil boom, there was evidence of oil in the lower Mackenzie Valley. In 1911, J. K. Cornwall, known as "Peace River Jim", had commissioned an Indian named Karkesee to look for oil seepages below the spot where coal measures have been burning along the river bank since before the time of Alexander Mackenzie. The Indian found pools of oil in the gravel of the river-bank to which he later guided Cornwall. Upon analysis, oil samples gathered by Cornwall were found to be similar to the oil produced in Pennsylvania.

In 1913, Cornwall succeeded in interesting J. H. Woods, publisher of the Calgary *Herald*, and Fred C. Lowes, Calgary real estate operator, in the project. They retained Dr. T. O. Bosworth, a geologist in the employ of the Shell Oil Company, who happened to be in Calgary at the time. The following summer Dr. Bosworth examined the seepages and, at the point where the Indian had taken Cornwall, supervised the staking of claims for his employers. He pointed out in his report that "it was the remarkable character of the Fort Creek shales and Beavertail limestone, rather than the seepages which led to a favourable view of the prospects of this field." Nevertheless, he also stated that near the mouth of what later was known as Bosworth Creek, "the seepages are conspicuous for a distance of two and a half miles. On digging into the river gravel, the outcrops of the green oil-sands are exposed and the oil could be collected in considerable amount."

The claims secured by the Cornwall syndicate were later bought by Imperial Oil Limited, and development was undertaken by a subsidiary, the Northwest Company. Theodore A. Link, later to become chief geologist for the Company, then a young man entrusted with his first important commission, was sent in 1919 to what later became known as Norman Wells to supervise the drilling.

The first well was spudded-in at a point near the mouth of Bosworth Creek; bedrock was reached under less than 20 feet of frozen glacial drift; at 83 feet, a flow of fresh water was struck below which the first showing of oil was encountered. This first oil-bearing stratum is known as the Imperial Formation, 255 feet thick at that point, through all of which some oil was found. Passing out of the Imperial Formation, the drill penetrated what is called the Fort Creek Shales, also oil-bearing; and, at a depth of 783 feet, drilling was discontinued because the flow of oil, at times shooting 75 feet in the air, seemed sufficient. (This Discovery well was deepened to 1,025 feet in 1923, still in the Fort Creek Shales). In the next few years, Northwest Company drilled five additional wells in the Norman Wells field, in all but one of which oil in various amounts was found.

Since no market existed for oil in the lower Mackenzie Valley, the wells were capped to await developments. This came from an unexpected quarter. In 1930, as we have seen, Gilbert LaBine staked the Eldorado mine, producing radium and uranium. The development of what eventually became a large enterprise created a need for fuel, which Imperial was in a position to supply. The Company reopened its wells and subsequently installed a refining plant with a capacity of 850 barrels a day. Although operated only in summer, this refinery was adequate until the United States entered the war, and then the whole picture changed.

Before the entry of the United States, the Canadian Government had completed construction of a line of airports between Edmonton and Whitehorse, Yukon Territory, within easy reach of Fairbanks, Alaska. Then after the entry of the United States, the U. S. Army had built a highway through Canadian territory to Alaska, with its northern terminal at Fairbanks. Soon both highway and airports were busy conveying war materials to Alaska and to the Soviet Union. For this, oil was required. Since tankers were not available to bring it in by way of the Pacific, the scheme known as the Canol Project (of which more later) was devised under which the Norman Wells production was expanded. The project also included a pipeline 600 miles long, crossing the Mackenzie Mountains to Whitehorse, and a refinery brought there from Texas to convert the crude into aviation gasoline and other necessary products.

When the Japanese were driven out of the Aleutians, and

99

oil requirements in northern Canada and Alaska relaxed considerably, drilling at Norman Wells was discontinued; and when the war ended the pipeline was scrapped. A total of 62 wells had been drilled in the Norman Wells field, of which 56—a very high percentage—were producers.

In addition to the drilling, a widespread prospecting program was undertaken. In 1942, thirteen geological survey parties were in the field, and in the next two years conducted a reconnaissance survey of the Mackenzie Valley from below Great Slave Lake to the Mackenzie Delta. The parties were flown to their assigned locations by U. S. Army transport planes, and were serviced and supervised by plane. This geological examination of the Mackenzie Valley constitutes one of the most extensive of its kind ever undertaken anywhere. Interestingly enough, it was planned and directed by Dr. T. A. Link, on loan from Imperial, who had drilled the first wells in the Mackenzie Valley. While wells were drilled only in the Norman Wells field (except for a few unsuccessful wildcats elsewhere), the geological information secured will be of inestimable value to those attempting to locate the oil which the survey disclosed as likely to be found in the structures underlying a great part of the Mackenzie Valley.

Here then, between Great Slave Lake and the Arctic Ocean, is a potential oilfield (or oilfields) of tremendous proportions. What about the area between Great Slave Lake and Turner Valley? This was the question that intrigued the oil-searchers. Working outward from Turner Valley, the drills ground into the earth, sometimes to find a little oil, more often to find gas in considerable quantities, but oftener still to find nothing. Many millions of dollars were spent in this way. Several of these wells reached depths of almost 12,000 feet—two miles down! Although the results were negative with respect to oil, the drilling helped to round out the geological picture.

With everything pointing to the existence of great pools of oil somewhere beneath the prairie soil, the geologists

were confident that sooner or later the drillers would tap
one of them. When, however, Imperial, in 1946, began drilling a well in the middle of a field at Leduc, about 16 miles
south of Edmonton, there was no greater indication than on
many other occasions that this time the greenish-black fluid
would blow out of the hole; but, on February 13, 1947, at a
depth of over 5,000 feet, that is what happened.

The boom that followed was not of the Calgary variety,
when thousands who knew nothing about oil mortgaged
their homes and jettisoned their savings in the hope of making a fortune. In the boom which followed the strike at
Leduc nothing but blue chips counted; the players were the
biggest oil companies in the world, and they were not playing for marbles.

Soon the once-peaceful countryside was studded with derricks, below which drills bored relentlessly into the earth.
Imperial naturally had the advantage in the Leduc field, but
other companies were not far behind. From the first, Leduc
gave every indication of being a major field, but only the
drill could determine its extent. That this might be considerable was shown in January, 1948, when Imperial again scored
in a well three miles north of Leduc in what has since been
called the Woodbend field—or extension.

Meanwhile, dozens of rigs were feverishly drilling at
Leduc. Atlantic Oil Company's well No. 3, drilled a mile
northeast of Imperial's Discovery well, was spudded-in about
the middle of January, 1948, and produced a gusher on
March 8, at a depth of 5,267 feet. The drillers pumped mud
and cement into the hole, stopping the flow, but soon gas
began to escape from cracks in the earth, and small oil-filled
craters appeared over an area of about 40 acres surrounding
the well. Then, early in May, the well tore loose, spouting
oil at the rate of 15,000 barrels a day, in addition to from
50 to 75 million cubic feet of gas.

The countryside was flooded with oil, rendering danger
from fire very great. At this juncture—on May 13,—the

Alberta Petroleum and Natural Gas Board assumed control and halted production at all wells to allow as much as possible of the flow of No. 3 to drain away through the pipeline already laid by Imperial from the field to the railway at Nisku, eight miles away.

In an attempt to stop the flow, the drillers forced a mixture of feathers, sawdust, cottonseed hulls, redwood shavings, and mud into the hole, as well as 10,000 bags of cement, but without much result. What eventually proved successful was the drilling of two directional relief wells, one from a point 700 feet west, and the other 700 feet south of No. 3. These were drilled at an angle in order to strike near the bottom of No. 3. This required very accurate work because angle-drilling is hard to control. While the relief wells were being drilled, about 700,000 barrels of water, pumped from the North Saskatchewan, a mile and a half away, were forced down Imperial's No. 48, a quarter of a mile to the west, but this was also without effect.

To complete the succession of misfortunes, in the first week of September, despite all precautions, flames shot up from the well to heights of from 400 to 800 feet. A great pall of smoke mushroomed 7,000 feet into the air, and within 20 minutes the whole 40 acres about the well was ablaze. Fortunately, by this time, the relief wells were approaching their mark. Water at the rate of 1,500 barrels an hour was pumped into the west well; gradually the oil that formerly shot from the casing was changed to steam; and within 60 hours from its outbreak the fire was smothered. Thus the most spectacular incident in the search for oil came to an end. It is estimated that during its six months' wild rampage No. 3 belched up 1,250,000 barrels of oil, most of which was recovered or pumped back into the earth; but, of course, the gas could not be salvaged.

In the meantime, with so much crude oil coming from the Leduc field, greater refinery capacity in Alberta was needed, and consequently Imperial bought the refinery at Whitehorse from the United States Government and moved it to Edmonton. About half of the 7,000-ton refinery was hauled by truck over the Alaska Highway, and the rest came by rail and ship through Skagway and Vancouver. Tearing down and re-erecting this huge structure was a big undertaking, but the refinery was formally opened on July 17, 1948. At first it was supplied by tank truck, but within a few months the pipeline was extended from Nisku.

The oil picture was changed greatly in September, 1948, when Imperial brought in the first well in what is known as the Redwater field, about 40 miles northeast of Edmonton. The depth of this well was 3,264 feet—much shallower than those at Leduc,—while the oil-bearing formation was three-and-a-half times the average thickness at Leduc. Other strikes followed quickly. The Golden Spike field, 22 miles southwest of Edmonton, was next, in February, 1949. Here the depth was 6,082 feet, but the oil-bearing zone was 545 feet thick. Another field brought in before the end of 1949, was at Excelsior, 15 miles north of Edmonton, where the depth was 3,830 feet.

By the end of 1950, Alberta had already put Canada in the ranks of the major producers. The Leduc field, with 320 wells at the beginning of 1950, had increased to 527, with established reserves of 200 million barrels. This had been far exceeded by Redwater, with 720 wells and reserves of 500 million barrels. Because of proration, owing to limited refining and marketing facilities, daily production of these two fields and their nearby extensions, although about 100,-000 barrels, was considerably short of potential capacity. Other fields were being discovered and older ones extended. From Pincher Creek, at the far southwestern corner of the Province, came reports of further promising developments; the Gulf Oil Company had drilled a successful well at Stettler, 80 miles southwest of Leduc, while the Socony Company had brought in a producer at Big Valley, thus extending the field farther to the south and east. At Lloydminster, on the

Alberta-Saskatchewan boundary, where a field had been in existence for some years, additional producing wells had been drilled, and the search had been extended to several other parts of Saskatchewan.

Perhaps of greater significance, Imperial had succeeded in getting oil in quantity at Normandville, 30 miles south of the town of Peace River, at a depth of 6,700 feet. Subsequently a well was drilled successfully by the Shell and British American companies at Whitelaw, 35 miles west of Peace River, suggesting that further Leducs and Redwaters might in time be found in the Peace River country.

The year 1950 was one of intense activity in exploration as well, and more than 100 different oil companies had parties in the field, not only in Alberta, but in Saskatchewan, northeastern British Columbia, and also in southern Maintoba.

This account of the eventual finding of oil on the Great Plains of Canada is given in detail as an illustration of the manner in which new oilfields are developed. Undoubtedly, the process will be continued with infinite variations for many years to come—until derricks dot much of the landscape over the 800,000 square miles which geologists consider favourable for the accumulation of oil, and pipelines form an intricate network.

With flush production, the question of marketing became a pressing one. To refine such quantities of oil in Alberta was out of the question because soon the local market would be glutted. It was also out of the question to ship very much of it by rail. The time had come for a pipeline to the largest available market—eastern Canada. On April 30, 1949, the International Pipe Line Company was incorporated by special Act of Parliament, with Dr. O. B. Hopkins, Vice-President of Imperial Oil Limited, as President. The company undertook to build a line from Edmonton, through Regina, to Superior, Wisconsin, at the head of Lake Superior. There the oil would be transferred to lake tankers during the navigation season and stored during the closed season. The total cost was estimated to be about $90 million, and the length of the pipe, 1,127 miles. Some objection had been raised in Canada because the terminus was in United States territory; but it was pointed out that to extend the line, as suggested, to Fort William would require an additional 121 miles of pipe, an additional capital charge of $10 million, and an increase of about $1 million a year in maintenance costs.

Six months were required to complete the first lap from Edmonton to Regina, and, on October 4, 1950, oil began to flow through the pipe. Two months later—on December 6— the line had not only been completed to Superior, but the first oil had also come through. The pipe is 20 inches in diameter for the first 450 miles; 16 inches for the next 340 miles; and 18 inches for the final 360 miles, in the United States. Nominal capacity is 95,000 barrels a day for the first 450 miles, and 70,000 barrels for the remainder, but by the use of "booster" pumps this can be increased to a maximum of 130,000 barrels a day.

This is merely the first of many pipelines that will eventually be needed. One will possibly be built southward to serve the middle-western States, and others will be built westward to the Pacific coast. During 1950, greater emphasis was placed on pipelines for the export of gas, with several rival companies competing for the right to build them.

Within less than three years, Canada's position has changed from one of almost complete dependence upon outside sources for petroleum products to one in which complete independence is in sight; Canada will soon join the ranks of exporting nations, both as regards oil and gas.

In any attempt to estimate the extent of the oil fields on the Great Plains, it must be remembered that the possible oil area extends north and south over 2,000 miles, and in its southern part may possibly be from 400 to 600 miles wide. The Leduc and Redwater fields are south of the geographical centre of Alberta, and it is 1,200 miles to the Arctic coast. A great part of this extensive region could become productive of oil or gas, or both.

The final test, of course, is the drill. Dr. Wallace A. Pratt, Vice-President, retired, of Standard Oil Company of New Jersey, who has spent his life locating oil fields, insists that the reason the United States produces 60 per cent of the world's oil is chiefly because that country has drilled proportionately more wells than any other. Of course the drill cannot find oil where none exists; but where thick deposits of sedimentary rocks are found that were laid down in ancient seas, the chances are usually very good. This basic requirement is fulfilled to a superlative degree in the great geosyncline lying to the east of the Rocky Mountains and their successors to the north in Canada.

Thus we have in the plains region the prospect of an oil-producing area extending over a much greater territory than any other in the world. If the Athabaska tar sands, although minus a great part of their former content, can still produce such quantities of oil as estimated above, we may be justified in considering the development of these oilfields as the most important economic event in the history of Canada.

10

The Heartland

THAT part of Canada which some day will be the most productive as well as the most densely populated, consists of a roughly triangular area, about 800 miles wide at its base and extending northward for 2,000 miles to its apex. It comprises most of the Prairie Provinces and that part of the District of Mackenzie lying between the edge of the Canadian Shield and the mountain ranges. Its eastern border is indented by such lakes as Winnipeg, Athabaska, Great Slave, and Great Bear; and it is watered by the Saskatchewan, Athabaska, Peace, and Mackenzie rivers and their tributaries. It has a mean temperature in July of 57° F., or warmer, which means that generally wherever soil and moisture are favourable crops, including wheat, can be grown.

This region includes the Prairie wheatlands, bordered on the north by a zone of parkland; waterpower, either in the area itself or immediately adjacent, capable of producing about 7,500,000 horsepower; coal amounting to 46,500 million tons in Alberta alone, with unknown quantities at various points along the foothills farther north; and a potential oil and gas region already described stretching from southern Alberta to the Arctic coast. The two chief requisites of a highly industrialized region are power and raw materials, and this region has both. While no iron ore of consequence has yet been found, copper, lead, and zinc can be secured from the nearby Canadian Shield; but the greatest source of raw materials will be petroleum and natural gas from which many hundreds of different products, from perfumes to motor car tires, are derived. Salt beds, several hundred feet thick, at Elk Point, in central Alberta, could also provide a basis for the manufacture of further chemical products.

Processing of foods should be an important industry. At present, most of the wheat and other grains are shipped out of the country in their natural state, and while large quantities will doubtless always be exported, there is no reason, since power is available, why a much greater proportion should not be converted into the final products. The milling industry is, of course, already an extensive one, but it could be considerably enlarged to meet the need for greater domestic consumption, while better transportation facilities would step up exports of manufactured goods. Meat-packing, also an important industry now, could likewise increase with a larger population and improvement in transportation. Recently, in some districts, many farmers have begun growing oil-bearing crops such as sunflowers and flax in considerable quantities, and a few small crushing plants have been established. This, including the culture and processing of soy beans, is an industry that could be expanded to become much greater than at present.

Next to power and raw materials, transportation is most important. Except for heavy industry—in which iron ore would need to be imported and the finished product shipped out,—most of this region is not so far from tidewater as to render transportation costs too serious an obstacle. On the west, low passes through the mountains render outlet to the Pacific relatively easy; on the east, Hudson Bay is not too distant; while, for manufactured articles that are light in relation to cost, the populous central Provinces are within reach.

The most pressing need is for an outlet from the Peace River country to the Pacific coast. At present, a wheat-grower near Dawson Creek, for example, must ship his wheat 495 miles to Edmonton, and then, if by CNR, a further 771 miles to Vancouver; while, if the CPR is used between Edmonton and Vancouver, the additional distance will be 836 miles.

The proposed extension of the PGE will bring the Peace River country within half the distance. That the people of this strategically-situated section of Canada are still denied this outlet points up one of Canada's weaknesses—the failure of Canadians sometimes to think nationally.

Factory workers are also essential; and while the region has few such people now, most of the developments suggested in this book will be impossible without a considerable increase in immigration. Food for the workers is also a must which this region can supply in abundance. Already the prairie region is Canada's granary, and it also produces meats of all kinds; while the large lakes along the edge of the Shield provide fish which for texture and taste are unexcelled anywhere in the world. Since, however, the most important part of The Heartland is the northern part, it is significant that the last large area of undeveloped agricultural land is also to be found here. In Saskatchewan, as has already been said, the area between the Saskatchewan and Churchill rivers contains extensive stretches of fine agricultural land which will push the limit of farming northward in that region. These lands, in addition to generally rich soil, have the advantage of greater rainfall than farther south, while days are longer during the growing season. Indeed, it is possible that this section may some day be considered the garden spot of Saskatchewan.

The Shield, with its limited agricultural possibilities, occupies almost half of Saskatchewan; but this is not true of Alberta, where only the northeastern corner of the Province is touched by the Shield. This means that the fertile soils, characteristic of the Prairie region, here extend far to the north, to include the great Peace River country, comprising not only northern Alberta but a section of northeastern British Columbia as well. This arable area extends even beyond what is generally known as the Peace River country practically to the south shore of Great Slave Lake, including the valleys of the Hay, Buffalo, and Little Buffalo rivers, which flow into Great Slave Lake.

Peace River drains an area of 117,110 square miles, extending north and south across almost six degrees of latitude, and east and west across more than 16 degrees of longitude. Its drainage basin contains what are probably the most productive wheat-lands on the continent; extensive forests comprising both pulpwood and merchantable timber; deposits of semi-anthracite and low-volatile bituminous coal; large areas suited to stock-raising; almost incalculable hydro-electric possibilities; and mineral and oil prospects the extent of which can only be surmised.

The greatest of the Mackenzie's tributaries, it is the only river in North America that cuts through the main chain of the Rocky Mountains. The Liard and the Peel, also tributaries of the Mackenzie, likewise draw their waters from both sides of the maintain chain, but each flows through a gap where one mountain range ends and the next begins. Thus the Liard skirts the northern escarpment of the Rocky Mountains, which there come to an end, while the Peel flows through the gap between the end of the Mackenzie Mountains, which succeed the Rockies, and the Richardson Mountains, farther to the northwest.

Two rivers, the Finlay, flowing southeasterly, and the Parsnip, flowing northwesterly, meet head-on at almost latitude 56° N., after which, as the Peace, the combined stream heads directly eastward through the Rocky Mountains. Near the western entrance to the pass stands Mount Selwyn, named in honor of one of the fathers of Canadian geology, and known as the Mountain of Gold because it was once believed to consist largely of gold-bearing quartz. Until the river debouches onto the Alberta Plateau, it is navigable for any sort of river craft; but at that point it enters a narrow, horseshoe-shaped canyon, dropping 270 feet in 20 miles through one of the most spectacular gorges on the continent. Some day, no doubt, the power in these falls will be har-

nessed; and when it is realized that within a short distance
are billions of tons of excellent coal, ranging up to semi-
anthracite, some idea of the power possibilities of this region
may be obtained. From the sources of the Finlay to its mouth
at Slave River, the Peace is 1,065 miles long, and 807 miles
from the confluence of the Finlay and Parsnip.

Hudson Hope is the first settlement below the canyon; Fort
St. John, founded in 1805 by traders of the Northwest Com-
pany, is 51 miles farther on. A few miles southeast of Fort
St. John, the Alaska Highway crosses by a great steel bridge.
Both Hudson Hope and Fort St. John are in that section of
British Columbia east of the Rockies, known as the Peace
River Block. From Fort St. John, the river flows easterly,
and then makes a wide curve to the south, past Dunvegan,
after which it straightens out for a long northward course.
Near the beginning of this northward stretch is the town of
Peace River, Alberta, 180 miles below Fort St. John, where
the Smoky, largest branch of the Peace, comes in from the
southwest.

Peace River town is the largest community on the river,
with a population of about 2,000. Once known as Peace River
Crossing, it is at the point where the Northern Alberta Railways branch crosses the river on its way to its present terminus, Hines Creek, 65 miles northwest of Peace River town,
and 382 miles from Edmonton. The valley here is about 700
feet below the level of the adjoining plateau and presents
a grandeur of view equalled in few places and surpassed
nowhere else in Canada. The valley is about six miles wide,
and the river-channel about three-quarters of a mile.

The people of Peace River town resent any suggestion that
a change in name might save a great deal of confusion, but
the time to make a change is before the place becomes much
larger. Hay River, farther north, is another case in point;
the same name is used to designate not only a river and the
region which it drains but two different settlements. As with
Peace River, it would be much less confusing if the settle-

ments were given distinctive names; in fact, it might be well to revert to the original Indian names.

From Peace River town, the river flows generally northward for about 250 miles, turning then to the eastward, and shortly afterward, the town of Vermilion, with a population of about 1,800, appears on the south bank. Sixty miles below Vermilion, the river, now deep and wide, plunges over the Vermilion Chutes, a combined rapid and fall with a total drop of 30 feet. Beyond the falls, the river flows slightly north of east for another 200 miles before losing itself in Slave River, about 30 miles below the latter's head in Lake Athabaska.

Before the coming of the railway, the Peace was an important highway, providing the only convenient way to get from one part of the country to the other. From Hudson Hope, head of navigation, to its mouth, a distance of 770 miles, except for Vermilion Chutes, the river is navigable for the usual type of river steamer. Above the Chutes the course is interrupted in places by islands and sandbars and subject to continual shifting of channel; but, despite this, the Peace is considered a good river for navigation, as such rivers go.

Until it reaches the lowlands, the Peace presents a panorama of scenic beauty. The Alberta Plateau slopes gently from the foothills until it merges into the Mackenzie Lowland; and the Peace, in cutting its channel across the plateau, has carved a mighty valley. Where it emerges from the mountains, the valley is 1,200 feet below the level of the adjacent country; but as it continues eastward, the banks gradually lower, until at Vermilion they are only 60 feet high; and before the river loses its identity in Slave River, they practically disappear. Its valley, from rim to rim, averages about three miles in width, and its channel, from 700 to 800 feet wide at Hudson Hope, varies from a half to three-quarters of a mile most of the way from Fort St. John to Vermilion, after which it is more often a mile wide.

According to Alexander Mackenzie, the Peace received its

name because on its bank (at Peace Point, 60 miles above its mouth), the Cree and Beaver Indians, traditional enemies, settled their quarrel, agreeing that thenceforth the river should be the boundary between them. Those who first explored it and its tributaries were furtraders, and until settlers began to take up homesteads in the years before the first world war, traders dominated the Peace River country. Although other traders were also there, its scattered communities were generally gathered about the posts established by the Hudson's Bay Company or its predecessor, the Northwest Company. The Hudson's Bay Company owned and operated most of the river boats; and, previous to the coming of the railway, travellers were largely dependent upon the Company for everything they required—food, shelter, and transportation.

The Edmonton, Dunvegan and British Columbia Railway, building northward from Edmonton, reached the town of Peace River in 1916. In the same year, an extension westward across the Smoky to Spirit River was built from McLennan, 50 miles south of Peace River. Another extension was built from Spirit River to Grande Prairie, 45 miles to the south, the principal town in the Peace River country. These extensions served a large area of partly settled country; but, as is usual in such cases, they resulted in causing settlers to venture farther afield. Consequently, while the older sections were supplied, however inadequately, with transportation, new thinly settled zones were created still beyond the railway's reach.

The railway company, never very strong financially, eventually came to the end of its resources; and in 1920 the Alberta Government, as guarantor of its securities, took over its lines and leased them to the CPR. Subsequently, these lines and those of the Alberta and Great Waterways Railway, connecting Edmonton with the Athabaska River at Waterways, were leased to the CPR and CNR jointly, and, under the name, Northern Alberta Railways, have since been operated by them. In 1922, the northern branch was extended from Peace River town to Hines Creek, north of Peace River; and between 1924 and 1930, the south branch was continued from Grande Prairie to its present terminus at Dawson Creek, 495 miles from Edmonton.

The country through which the Peace runs is the last wheat-growing area of any extent on the North American continent. Although wheat grown in the Peace River country has the longest haul of any in Canada, the number of elevators to be seen along the railway lines is a good indication of what the land will produce. As early as 1896, and more than once since, the world's prize has been won by grain grown in the Peace River country. The region is also excellent for stock-raising, which is the only kind of farming possible where the distance from the railway prevents the marketing of grain. As Alexander Mackenzie passed up the river in 1792-93, he saw herds of buffalo and elk grazing on its banks, and for many years the Peace River country supplied meat for points farther east. In 1830, dried meat amounting to 37,386 pounds was shipped from Dunvegan alone. The Peace River country, like other parts of Canada, merely awaits the coming of people to provide an abundance of everything needed for comfortable and prosperous homes.

North of what is commonly called the Peace River country, and practically continuous with it, is another large area drained by the Hay, Fort Nelson, and Liard Rivers. This region is cut by the 60th parallel, and is therefore partly in the Provinces of Alberta and British Columbia and partly in the District of Mackenzie. Its soil varies, and in some sections large areas consist of swamp, but, in general, it is good arable land. Perhaps the best indication of its quality is that its eastern portion has been set aside as a national park for the preservation of the last remaining wild buffalo on the North American continent. Here, the wood-buffalo, augmented by others brought in from herds at Wainwright and elsewhere, have roamed and multiplied for years. These animals forage for themselves, both summer and winter, which they could not do if, season after season, the country did not provide a sufficient growth to support them. This region by itself would not provide suitable homes for settlers because of its remoteness from outside markets; but since it lies within easy reach of the mining regions about Lake Athabaska and Great Slave Lake, settlers on these lands should before long be able to count on an established market for any supplies they might produce. Furthermore, there is a very good chance that oil will be found in this region which, with minerals not far away, might result in important industries.

Because the mountains encroach on the west, agricultural possibilities in the Mackenzie Valley below the Liard are more restricted; and, on the east, the Shield is quite close; but many pockets of arable land exist along the Mackenzie itself and in the lower reaches of some of its tributaries; and these can be utilized to provide food for those engaged in developing the oil and other resources of that part of the Valley.

While, in sketching in the future industrial possibilities of this region, the primary position is given to petroleum—which includes the Athabaska tar sands,—nothing has yet been said of possible developments in the field of atomic energy and the use of uranium products in industry. At present the chief source of uranium is the Eldorado mine, concentrates from which are shipped for refining to Port Hope, Ontario. These, and concentrates from other deposits since discovered near the eastern end of Lake Athabaska and elsewhere might more easily be shipped to a refinery established somewhere in the Peace River country, which would save the long haul to Port Hope. Not only could radium be produced there, but other products of pitchblende as well. Because of the existence of so many intangibles, it is obviously not possible to do more than suggest these possibilities; but each line of manufacturing that can be carried on within the area makes possible the establishment of others. Only by means of quantity and variety can transportation costs be kept to a point where full advantage can be taken of the other factors—power and raw materials.

This chapter may seem to be a departure from the general thesis of the book—that northern Canada is mainly the part which, if ever, will justify the assertion that the twentieth century is Canada's. The prairie region is included in it because no definite physiographic break exists between north and south, although up to a point, potential productivity increases as a rule with northerliness. Furthermore, raw materials from the North will stimulate industry all over the Prairies, while prairie products will find a ready market in the North. It is more than possible, however, that the greatest agricultural production and the greatest industrial concentration will eventually both be in northern Alberta. And when I say *northern* Alberta, I mean probably somewhere in the Peace River country. This, of course, is looking many years ahead—how many is the big question; but I believe that the outlines of the picture of what the future holds are already taking shape.

Edmonton, now generally thought of as in *northern* Alberta, is in reality near the southern edge of that part of Alberta which has the greatest future possibilities, but it is unlikely that any other city will ever surpass it. Edmonton's superb location on the North Saskatchewan River, the main east-west natural highway, will help to keep it in the lead, especially since it will continue to be the Gateway to the North. Furthermore, the fact that it is already surrounded by producing oilfields, and is now an important refining centre, with prospects of becoming a much greater one, is sufficient in itself to ensure a great future for Edmonton. It also has another feature, which cities farther north might eventually also have, and that is its outlet to the Pacific through both Vancouver and Prince Rupert. Hitherto, as we have seen,

Prince Rupert has not counted for a great deal in the Canadian economy; but this will certainly not continue if Canada should take the course that now seems likely.

Because Edmonton is on the North Saskatchewan, it became an early traffic-centre; by 1875, the first river-steamers had reached there. Ten years later, a road was built the 100 miles to Athabaska Landing, giving access to the Mackenzie Valley, which ended the canoe-route by way of Methye Portage. With the building of the CPR through Calgary, 200 miles to the south, the latter became the principal centre of what was later the Province of Alberta; and although a branch from Calgary reached the south bank of the river, opposite Edmonton, at what was then called Strathcona, in 1895, Edmonton was still more or less out on the end of a limb. This was changed in 1905 when the Canadian Northern reached the city from the east; and in the same year Alberta became a Province and Edmonton its Capital. Edmonton's situation was considerably improved a few years later when the Canadian Northern and Grand Trunk Pacific were built through to the Pacific coast, but Edmonton was still on the northern fringe of settlement.

The trek of settlers into the Peace River country during the early years of the century, and the sporadic railway building which occurred in that same region helped Edmonton somewhat; but the high hopes that were then prematurely generated, as is usual in such circumstances, were so completely dashed when the boom inevitably burst that Edmonton was years in recovering.

Gilbert LaBine's discovery of pitchblende at Great Bear Lake in 1930, and the spectacular rise of Yellowknife a few years later, combined to push Edmonton again to the front rank. During the second world war, Edmonton was one of the busiest spots in Canada, especially after the United States declared war on Japan. This, as we have seen, resulted in the building of the Alaska Highway and the development of the Canol Project, for both of which Edmonton was the port of entry. Hundreds of thousands of American military personnel funnelled through the city, and many others established headquarters there, imposing added strain upon already overtaxed housing and office facilities. Edmonton was the gate through which passed the supplies and equipment needed for these projects; and during this period Edmonton literally bulged at the seams. Its airport broke world's records, which at intervals it has continued to do. For years, of all the hotels in Canada, the CNR's Macdonald was the most difficult in which to get a room-reservation. This is being remedied somewhat by an addition of 16 storeys which will add 300 rooms to the hotel.

Edmonton has for some time been the fastest-growing city in Canada, and it is hard to see any reasonable limit to its size. Owing to the enthusiasm of its people in the past, it is said to have the largest area of any city in Canada except Montreal; and it is just possible that eventually it will hold a similar position with respect to population. The question seems to be: will Edmonton become the second-largest city in Canada, or only the third? There are some in the West who contend that if Edmonton must take third place it will be to Vancouver, not Toronto, and this is not based merely on bombast. Since Vancouver is a seaport, and the nearest to Edmonton, it will naturally increase in size and importance with Edmonton, because a great deal of what is tributary to Edmonton is tributary also to Vancouver—while Vancouver has resources that are not shared with Edmonton. Perhaps enough has been said to indicate that Edmonton is one of the great cities of the future.

The northern half of Alberta will not, however, remain for long a single-city region. For one thing, the distance between what must one day be the highly industrialized region near or adjacent to Lake Athabaska and Great Slave Lake and Edmonton will be too great, and a nearer centre will develop. In this regard, Vermilion seems indicated, although the town of Peace River is also a likely candidate, but pos-

sibly too far south and west. Vermilion is about 350 miles
north of Edmonton in a direct line, while Peace River is about
250 miles.

In this particular area, three jurisdictions overlap; the
Province of Alberta, east of longitude 120° W., and British
Columbia west of that line, are the governing authorities
south of latitude 60°; while the Federal Government is responsible north of that latitude. Many of the services needed
in both sections require joint action by at least two governments; and while, in most cases, so far, co-operation has been
forthcoming—as with the highway from Grimshaw to Hay
River,—this may not always be the case. The mines and the
oilfields will be developed by large corporations, many of
them, especially in the oilfields, dominated by United States
capital. These corporations will be guided, of course, by considerations of profit, which is to be expected; but services
will be needed which, although not immediately profitable,
will be essential for the orderly and, in the long run, socially-
profitable development of the country; for, after all, if the
country does not provide homes for people in which they can
live comfortable and socially-useful lives, it will fail of its
purpose. Matters such as these will need to be planned, and
in some cases provided in advance of their actual need. This
will require some sort of joint planning agency which is not
yet in sight. And if the suggestion of a highway to Asia put
forth in a later chapter should ever be seriously considered,
then an additional agency might be needed which would include American and, eventually, let us hope, Soviet representatives as well.

Finally, none of the developments referred to here will be
possible in their entirety unless many more people are
allowed to enter Canada. The opening up of the West that
followed the building of the CPR was made possible by the
great influx of immigrants who poured into the country in
the early years of the century; and the North will not be

adequately opened up without more people to draw from. Unfortunately, as a backwash of European strife, prejudices have arisen against people of some nationalities. The most reliable test in such matters, however, is experience; and on that basis it can safely be said that, on the whole, Canada has little to fear—and much to gain—from the immigrant, from wherever he may hail. She can confidently assume that those who come to her shores will repay with interest any trust that may be reposed in them.

It may seem to some that, in making the assertion that this region, now so empty and largely undeveloped, may some day become the most populous and important industrial region of Canada, I am indulging in some of the wishful-thinking of which I have accused others; but the situation is much different now from what it was at the turn of the century. At that time, the economic significance of petroleum, for example, was not apparent. The motor car, with its great demand for gasoline and lubricating oils, was still in the experimental stage. The airplane was even more so; the internal combustion engine which, for so many, has since revolutionized the conditions of life, had not yet found its place.

The steam locomotive, for generations the highest manifestation of steam's utility, having first adopted fuel oil in place of coal, has now given way to the Diesel-electric engine in which the motive-power is provided entirely by oil. And now the gas-turbine and jet-propulsion are possibilities of the near future—to say nothing of atomic energy!

In this petroleum age, any country with the potential production of the region referred to in this chapter, plus all its other resources and advantages, can only fail to become a great industrial region because of a lack of appreciation concerning its possibilities. If this appreciation were to depend solely upon the people who live there, development of the country would speedily follow; for it cannot truthfully be said that the people of any part of the West, and especially of this section, harbour any doubts concerning the value of their own country. But unfortunately the proper development of this region is more than a local matter; it will depend also upon how fully Canadians as a whole realize its importance to their welfare and to the welfare of Canada.

11

The Last Great West

THE western frontier has always held a fascination for the people of Canada and the United States, and it has played an important part in the history of both countries. In the United States, except for the myths that come out of Hollywood, the western frontier has disappeared forever; but it still survives in Canada. Although Calgary, with its annual Stampede, would give the impression that the frontier still lives along the foothills of the Rockies, it must be admitted that the frontier has gone from that region too. Bits of the frontier may still be found in some parts of the Peace River country; but to find any extensive area in which is still holds sway you must go to the rolling uplands of the northern British Columbia interior, where the range is still unhedged by fences, and real cowboys ride herd on real range cattle.

British Columbia has been called a "sea of mountains," and at a superficial glance the term seems apt enough; it certainly is a jumble of mountains, seemingly thrown up in the most haphazard manner, with little elbow-room for people, and no hope of anything but primitive frontier conditions. That, however, is not correct. While on the map, and even to a person criss-crossing the country by plane, it may seem a jumble, the mountains can be sorted into a system.

In the first place, the mountains mostly run in a northwest-southeast direction, and this is parallel to the edge of the Canadian Shield and to the Pacific coastline. Then, according to the type of rocks out of which they are built, they can be divided into three distinct zones. Those on the east, the ones that can be seen from the Prairies, known as the Rocky Mountains, consist almost entirely of sedimentary rocks. This means, too, that they are comparatively young, as mountains go, which is shown by their sharp, jagged peaks, so recently uplifted that they have not yet been rounded by time. Even an amateur geologist can see that they are composed of the same sort of rocks that floor the Plains. Once they, too, were horizontal; but when the mountains were crumpled into being they were pushed up on edge, some almost perpendicular, or else tilted at a sharp angle.

It is not hard to distinguish these mountains from those that come next on the west, occupying a belt about 200 miles wide and extending from the southern to the northern border of British Columbia. They are generally not so high as the Rockies because, being older, frost and water have worn more of them away. They differ from the Rockies in yet another way since they are composed not only of sedimentary rocks, but also of hard, granitic rocks caused by molten masses welling up from deep down in the earth. They consist of many groups: in the south, they are known as the Columbia Mountains, of which the Selkirks and Monashee Mountains are a part; farther north, come the Cariboo Mountains; and beyond these, the Cassiar Mountains.

Lying between the Rockies and the Columbia and Cariboo Mountains is the Rocky Mountain Trench, one of the most remarkable physiographic features on the continent. Beginning south of the International Boundary, it extends northwestward through British Columbia for about 900 miles, its floor from 2,000 to 3,000 feet above sea level, and varying in width from two to ten miles. Most of the great rivers that flow from the western flank of the Rocky Mountains take their rise in the Rocky Mountain Trench.

Between the mountain masses, sometimes forming elevated bases upon which mountains stand, uplands or plateaus, ranging from 2,000 to 5,000 feet above sea level, comprise a large part of the interior of British Columbia.

123

Finally, in the far west, are the Coast Mountains, likewise occupying a belt about 200 miles in width, bordering on the Pacific. Near the United States border and south of it, they are called the Cascades; farther north, they become much higher until they merge with the St. Elias Mountains in the northwestern corner of the Province, the tallest peak of which, Mount Logan, in Yukon Territory, is 19,850 feet high. What this means may be comprehended somewhat by comparison with the highest that the Rockies have to offer—Mount Robson's 12,792 feet. Those who have attempted, as the CNR train stops momentarily, to get a glimpse of Robson's often cloud-shrouded peak may imagine what it would look like if it stood a mile and a quarter nearer the sky! Aside from their general height, the Coast Mountains differ from their neighbours to the east in that they consist almost entirely of granitic rocks.

Thus, the Rockies consist, as already said, principally of sedimentary rocks; and the Coast Mountains, going to the other extreme, are mostly made up of the harder rocks; while the mountains of the interior consist of both classes of rocks. But it is because the mountains of British Columbia consist so largely of the hard, intrusive rocks that the interior of the Province has such varied mineral resources, while the sedimentary Rockies produce coal.

As might be expected from a mountainous land, the lakes of British Columbia are long and narrow—and very beautiful. In the south, the Kootenay, Arrow, and Okanagan Lakes occupy parallel valleys. Farther north, Stuart, Takla, Babine, and Francois Lakes occupy a broad, central upland region; while in the northwestern corner of the province, a most remarkable group of beautiful lakes lie partly in British Columbia and partly in Yukon Territory. This group, consisting of Tagish, Atlin, and Teslin, with mountains rising from the edge of deep, clear water, will surely attract the attention some day that their beauty deserves.

With mountains running northwest and southeast, and

lakes lying in the same general direction, it would be strange if the rivers did not also follow the same general pattern. This they do; and yet they also display a curious tendency to work their way westward, although there is one interesting exception. As already mentioned, most of the large rivers rise in the Rocky Mountain Trench: the Kootenay, the most southerly of these, flows southward into the United States, then loops back into British Columbia, and, after passing through Kootenay Lake, flows westward into the Columbia. In its turn, the Columbia rises in the Trench, flows northwestward for 250 miles, and then breaks out to the west and south at the Big Bend, eventually to reach the Pacific through the United States. Likewise the Fraser, farther north, follows almost the same pattern. The Peace, however, as we have seen, is formed by two rivers which rise in the Trench, but it then flows eastward to swell the mighty Mackenzie.

In the northwestern part of the Province, the rivers are shorter and flow more or less directly westward to the Pacific; but the two principal ones, the Skeena and Stikine, like the Fraser and Columbia, first flow northwestward, make a bend to the south, and then swing westward. This, then, seems to be the pattern of most British Columbia rivers: they flow northwestward along one side of a mountain range, bend round its end, and flow southward along the opposite side, eventually working their way westward to the ocean.

Next to British Columbia's mountains, the characteristic with which most people are familiar—or think they are!—is its climate. Ask any dozen Easterners who have never been to British Columbia what its climate is like, and ten will say that it is mild and moist, which, most of the time, is quite correct for a very small part of the province—that lying near the coast. But, east of the mountains that fringe the coast, the climate is neither mild nor moist. There are many places in the interior valleys where the thermometer reaches 100°F. in the shade, and even higher, in summer, and goes down to 50° and 60° below zero in winter. So much for mildness.

There is a place on the west coast of Vancouver Island where the average annual rainfall is 200 inches, while less than 200 miles to the east, there are places where it is less than 10 inches—which is considered by climatologists to be a desert condition. Over large areas in the southern interior of British Columbia sage brush and cactus, accompanied by rattlesnakes, are as common as they are in Arizona.

The reason for these apparent freaks of nature is very easily explained. The prevailing winds, loaded with moisture, come off the Pacific, generally the North Pacific, and across the country in a southeasterly direction. Then, in passing over the first mountains, they lose most of their moisture in the form of rain or snow, which falls on the western slope, so that by the time the winds reach the interior valleys they are both dry and hot. In passing eastward, they again pick up moisture through evaporation, which is once more dropped in crossing the Rockies; and, again hot and dry, the winds emerge onto the prairies. Under certain conditions, these winds, then called Chinooks, have been known to absorb a foot of snow in a few hours.

This varied climate naturally has a considerable influence on the kind of crops that can be grown in British Columbia. On the coast, most crops grow well except those, like wheat, that are too little suited to rain; and consequently hay crops do better than cereals. This means that many farmers go in for dairying and the growing of certain varieties of fruits, especially berries. In the dry sections, no crop at all can be grown without irrigation, as in the Okanagan and Kootenay valleys. On the other hand, where water for irrigation can be obtained, fine fruits and vegetables are the rule. On the higher land, where water cannot be secured, or where the soil is not quite so fertile, ranches are found, as is also the case in those sections too far from the railway for successful farming. On the northern interior uplands, as already mentioned, a number of the largest cattle ranches in Canada can

Saw-log Boom, Giscome, E

be seen, some of the principal ones on the Chilcotin Plateau, west of the Fraser River.

As compared with the Prairie regions, British Columbia is not primarily an agricultural Province, although her river valleys and rolling uplands contain considerable areas of arable land. In many places the land requires much heavy clearing, although in certain places the timber can be turned to advantage. In some sections, arrangements have been made by the Government for large-scale clearing of available tracts by the use of modern power equipment, at a minimum cost to the settler.

Minerals and timber are the two chief resources of British Columbia's interior, varying with the locality. The Kootenay and Okanagan valleys both produce fine fruit, while the former is also an important mining region. Among other mines it has the great Sullivan mine at Kimberley which, with the smelter at Trail, is owned by Consolidated Mining and Smelting Company of Canada Limited. Since these regions are already well known, even to people in other Provinces, I shall therefore devote more attention to the less-known northern parts of the Province.

It was the northern part of British Columbia that first attracted world attention when, in 1861, heavy placer gold was discovered in the gravels of a creek in the far interior. This creek, later called Williams Creek, is a branch of a tributary of the Fraser, flowing in from the south about 500 miles above the Fraser's mouth. At that time British Columbia was still a struggling Crown Colony, with but a few thousand people living mostly in Victoria, at the southern end of Vancouver Island, and in the lower Fraser Valley. A few years before, gold had been discovered in California, causing many thousands of gold-seekers and others to flock there. Most of them were disappointed and soon moved away, but many remained in California, hoping for another

Land near Smithers, B.C.

chance at fortune, and they stampeded to British Columbia when fine gold was found in sandbars on the lower Fraser.

Consequently, when word of the gold-strike in what came to be known as the Cariboo trickled out to the coast, one of the world's most picturesque gold rushes was on. Disappointed miners still hanging about the San Francisco waterfront, in towns farther north, or disconsolately working the lean bars of the Fraser, rushed to the new diggings. Ships could sail up the Fraser as far as Yale, at the foot of the Fraser Canyon, where the river breaks through the Cascade Range. Dumped on shore there, the gold-seekers were faced with a trip of 500 miles, following the precipitous slopes of the Fraser, crossing mountains, and traversing thickly timbered valleys, in many places almost impassable because of windfalls. Yet they struggled on; and within a few months an almost continuous line of men, pack on back, pushed through the wilderness in the hope of finding the glittering metal that they had heard could be picked out of the gravel in chunks.

Soon a trail was cut through, and then began endless trains of horses and mules—and, for a time, even camels!—carrying supplies of all sorts for the thousands of miners who quickly reached the Cariboo. The diggings were not only in the bed of Williams Creek, but extended to a score of other creeks within a radius of 20 miles. Nearly everyone fortunate enough to file a claim in the upper reaches of Williams Creek, on several of its branches, or on Lightning, Antler, or Grouse, became wealthy almost overnight. Usually the gold, sometimes in fairly large nuggets, was on the bedrock, only a few feet below the surface, covered by a layer of coarse gravel, while finer gold-dust was found in the gravel. Mining operations were of the simplest, requiring little equipment that could not be made on the spot.

In the early sixties, the towns along the bed of Williams Creek—Richfield, Barkerville, Camerontown,—contained more people than were in all the rest of British Columbia.

Soon the capacity of the pack-trail was taxed to the limit, and Governor Douglas, with assistance from the British Government, undertook to build a wagon road from Yale to Barkerville. The British Government's contribution consisted chiefly of a company of Royal Engineers, whose varied skills were of great assistance to the struggling colony. And in a day when all supplies must come by way of the Horn, and before the invention of dynamite, the Cariboo Road was almost as great an achievement as the building of the Panama Canal half a century later. Over it a steady procession of horse-, mule-, and ox-teams, and horse- and mule-trains passed, while horse-drawn stagecoaches carried passengers and mail. The road, over 400 miles in length, was completed at a cost of $1,000,000 (paid for by tolls), two years before Confederation, and six years before British Columbia became part of Canada.

As is usual with such booms, the great bulk of the prospectors were eventually disappointed; and all but the lucky ones moved on, except for the inevitable few who never lose hope. Gradually, over the years, the two principal towns, Barkerville and Van Winkle (Stanley), although they never ceased to produce gold, were reduced to virtual ghost-towns. Strangely enough, Cariboo oldtimers, backed it is true by geological opinion at the time, were firm in their belief that such quartz ledges as remained were barren. In fact, for a long time a quartz miner was as unpopular in Barkerville as a sheep man is in a cattle country. Then, about 1930, came Fred Wells, who, despite great discouragement, developed the Cariboo Gold Quartz mine at Jack of Clubs Lake and proved that at least some of the ore that had produced the placers was still in Cariboo. This gave the region a new lease on life, built the town of Wells, and has even to a certain extent revived the decaying town of Barkerville.

When the CPR was built through in 1885, it cut the Cariboo Road at Ashcroft, which then supplanted Yale as the terminus, and the section between Ashcroft and Yale fell into disuse. Until the motor car arrived, the picturesque stagecoach shuttled between Ashcroft and Barkerville, over what for many years was the longest stageline of its kind in the world. In recent years, the Ashcroft-Yale section has been restored, and now buses make daily trips from Vancouver far into the interior.

Until about 1915, the mainline of the CPR was the only railway across British Columbia; and since that line traverses the southern part of the province, it was natural that most development should be confined to that section. An opportunity to broaden this restricted area of development seemed to be coming when the Grand Trunk Pacific was built to a new port at Prince Rupert. The completion of the railway coincided, however, with the first world war and the bankruptcy of the Grand Trunk. In the meantime, a third transcontinental railway, the Canadian Northern, had reached the coast. Building westward from Edmonton, like the Grand Trunk Pacific, also through Yellowhead Pass, instead of proceeding to some northern port, it turned southwestward along the North Thompson to Kamloops, thence paralleling the CPR to Vancouver.

A few years later, the Grand Trunk Pacific and the Canadian Northern were consolidated into the Canadian National Railways System; Vancouver became its principal Pacific terminus; and Prince Rupert was virtually neglected. If the CNR had not had the choice of two ports, and had been compelled to concentrate its attention on Prince Rupert, the history of the northern interior of British Columbia might have been very different. On the other hand, since it is not the principal function of a railway to undertake the development of the country through which it runs; and since, in the past, greater traffic has undoubtedly been available in the southern part of the province, the CNR cannot be blamed for devoting its major attention to the most productive part of its territory. This, however, has resulted in a generation of stagnation for Prince Rupert and the great valleys and uplands of northern British Columbia. Without a national policy, to which the Province also subscribed, there was little chance to develop the area of which Prince Rupert is the natural outlet. Yet, without such a policy, the Grand Trunk Railway scheme, embarked upon with such a fanfare in 1903, was from the start doomed to failure.

Even the builders of the Grand Trunk Pacific realized that, in the circumstances, many years must elapse before Prince Rupert could become an important seaport, and the country adjacent to it sufficiently productive to supply needed traffic. They accordingly arranged for the building of the Pacific Great Eastern Railway from Prince George, on their mainline about midway between Edmonton and Prince Rupert, to Vancouver. But before this line was more than begun, the Grand Trunk Pacific and the Pacific Great Eastern had both passed into receiverships. The former was taken over by the Government of Canada, and the latter by the British Columbia Government, guarantors, respectively, of their bonds.

The PGE, which started at Squamish, on Howe Sound, 40 miles short of its southern terminus at Vancouver, had reached Quesnel, 84 miles short of its northern terminus at Prince George, when construction stopped. Thus, for thirty years, the PGE was a road with neither beginning nor end. Finally, in 1949, after many false starts, construction was resumed beyond Quesnel, this time with every prospect that the line would be completed to Prince George. Not only that, but there seems good reason to believe that its southern end will be at North Vancouver, while its northern end will be continued through the Rockies to a junction with the Northern Alberta Railways at Dawson Creek, thus providing the Peace River country with its long-hoped-for Pacific outlet.

The Fraser is the great river of British Columbia. Rising in the Rocky Mountain Trench, not far from the western entrance to Yellowhead Pass, it flows northwestward along

131

the Trench for 200 miles, and then makes a wide bend to the west and south. At the top of this bend, it comes to within a few miles of the headwaters of the Parsnip, southern branch of the Peace. The Nechako comes in from the northwest near the point where the Fraser begins a generally southward stretch, and here, in the angle between the two rivers, is located the city of Prince George, originally the Hudson's Bay Company's post of Fort George. The CNR line, which in general follows the river valley from Yellowhead Pass, now crosses the Fraser and continues up the Nechako.

Flowing almost due south from Prince George, and cutting a deep gash across the face of the Province, the Fraser seems to ignore the trend of the country until, within a short distance of the Province's southern boundary, it swings to the westward, cuts through the Cascades, and pours its silt-laden torrent into the Gulf of Georgia. For the whole of its turbulent 850 miles, the Fraser is a swift-flowing stream.

Quesnel, about 90 miles by river south of Prince George, may be taken as the southernmost point of the region that this book is designed more particularly to discuss. It is beautifully situated on the east bank of the Fraser, where the clear water of Quesnel River lends a riband of blue to the adobe-coloured Fraser. The once-famous Cariboo placer diggings are about 60 miles to the east, in a mountainous area not suited to agriculture. West of the Fraser, a fine farming region extends almost to the foothills of the Coast Mountains. Here are many long, beautiful lakes fed by mountain streams, leading to large rivers. It is a splendid ranching country, but with better transportation probably will ultimately be given over to mixed farming. Some day a railway should be built through this region to Bella Coola, on the coast. The whole of this territory is fairly heavily timbered; adjacent to Quesnel it is estimated that about 9,000,000,000 feet can be secured, much of it of merchantable quality, the rest suited to pulp. A plywood plant is already in operation in Quesnel, and a pulp mill is a possibility pending the completion of the

B. C. Power Commission's projected hydroelectric installation on the Quesnel River. The greater part of this country is covered by a thick mantle of glacial deposit, which makes prospecting difficult, but widespread evidences of minerals nevertheless exist, which should some day result in producing mines.

Most of the resources tributary to Quesnel are also found in the country about Prince George, which has the added advantage of being an important railway centre if and when the PGE is extended to Peace River, and especially if it should continue to Alaska as well. As we have seen, the CNR crosses the Fraser at Prince George and proceeds westward along the Nechako to where the latter bends to the southwest. Thence, by way of Fraser Lake and Endako River, it traverses the Bulkley Valley, and on to Hazelton, at the head of navigation on the Skeena. From here the railway follows the north side of the Skeena southwestward to within a few miles of Prince Rupert.

Prince George, already an important lumbering centre, with many sawmills along the CNR line, both east and west, should also in time have pulp mills, plywood, and other wood-processing plants. It is now, and seems destined to continue, the distributing point for most of the country extending northwestward to Hazelton, and eastward to the Rocky Mountains.

Despite Prince George's dominance, several important places—such as Vanderhoof, Burns Lake and Smithers—have grown up between Prince George and Hazelton, serving large adjacent areas consisting of rolling upland which some day will support a relatively large population.

There is much to suggest that this region should ultimately become a highly productive mining area. Gold, silver, copper, lead, zinc, and coal are found at a number of places, especially near Hazelton and Smithers, and many prospects await improved transportation facilities. The Groundhog coalfields, 100 miles northeast of Hazelton, contain large deposits of anthracite coal, which might suggest a future industrial region, since many of the essentials are present.

Owing to the wide area suited to stockraising and mixed farming, this region should some day produce large quantities of livestock. It is one of the few spots left where a settler with a pioneer spirit may find a remote valley through which a small clear stream leads to a lake, where there is range for cattle and horses, and where, sometimes in the early morning, he may see a moose munching lily pads, while playful bears are likely to come to the door for a handout.

Except for the Torngat Mountains along the Atlantic in Labrador, the Appalachians, dividing Quebec from Maine and extending into the Gaspé Peninsula, and the Laurentians, by courtesy called mountains, Canada, east of the Rockies, is a land of relatively low elevation. For this reason, most Canadians know little about mountains and when they contemplate a country like British Columbia, they are apt to be more than a little bewildered. Because mountains do not lend themselves to cultivation and close settlement, many people are inclined to consider them a total loss. It is true that in many ways mountains increase the difficulty of settlement. It is much harder to build roads or railways in a mountainous country; but when once they are built they often prove more satisfactory than elsewhere because they usually rest on foundations of rock. The first cost may be high, but too often people seem to forget that a country, whether mountain or plain, once conquered from the wilderness is, with proper conservation, an asset forever.

Few will argue, in this day of tourism, that scenery is a thing to be scorned; and in this regard the value of mountains cannot be computed in any known currency. But they have a much more vital use than that. The Saskatchewan, which drains the greater part of the Prairie region; the Peace and Athabaska, which drain the Peace River country; the Fraser and Columbia, whose waters nurture British Columbia's valleys, all have their sources in the Rocky Mountains; and every mountain range throughout the Province has its streams and lakes to which it supplies water from the snows on its crest. Therefore, as long as the mountains endure there is an assurance that this land will never lack life-giving water. It is the well-watered lands that have contributed most to civilization; life stands still in the desert.

Then there is the question of timber. Much lamentation is heard about the disappearance of the white pine forests of Ontario, and rightly so; but, as a matter of fact, over some of the area that once grew pine the land is too valuable to be cropped only once in a century. It was therefore inevitable that sooner or later those fertile lands should have become fields planted to more profitable crops. But the mountain slopes will never be given over to the plough; and if their timber is conserved, they, along with other land in various parts of the country, also unsuited to field crops, can supply the timber needs of the Canadian people forever.

One other objection is raised to mountains: they are looked upon as barriers to traffic; and this, at first, seems a vital objection in a country where transportation is all-important. But even on the prairies, traffic follows only certain routes; and in the mountains the passes are the natural routes. It is true that the CPR mainline, in crossing the Rockies, climbs to a maximum of 5,337 feet above sea level; but the highest elevation in Yellowhead Pass is 3,717 feet; in Pine Pass, it is 2,850 feet; and in Peace Pass, a water-grade can be secured at an elevation of about 2,000 feet.

12

Where Mountains Meet the Sea

MOUNTAINS have a fascination for many people, and so has the sea; but perhaps the spot with the greatest fascination of all is where mountains meet the sea. In this regard, the coastline of British Columbia is unmatched anywhere in the world. According to the map, its length is about 600 miles; but, following the shore, it is more than ten times that distance. Here stand mountain peaks bearing mantles of perpetual snow, their forest-clad flanks showing dark-blue in the distance; while, in some of the southern valleys, grow trees among the largest to be found on earth. Winding between the bases of these mountains, narrow arms of the sea, dotted with wooded islets, reach far inland, in some places more than 100 miles, presenting at every turn perfect vistas of landscape and water. Forming the western horizon, a line of tree-clad islands shimmers in the haze, each the top of a mountain partly buried beneath the waves. Between these off-lying islands and the mainland shore is the famous Inside Passage along which ships sail from Vancouver and other lower mainland ports, safe from Pacific swells, flanked on either side by mountain scenery, to Prince Rupert and ports in southeastern Alaska.

Vancouver Island, the largest of these outliers, 285 miles long by from 40 to 80 miles wide, is more than five times as large as Prince Edward Island. While it has the delightful climate familiar to people who know Victoria, at its southern end, it also has, in some places, the heaviest rainfall outside the tropics. Next in size to Vancouver Island are the Queen

136

Charlotte Islands, about 150 miles to the northwest, consisting of two larger islands and about 150 smaller ones. Rain is also plentiful on the Queen Charlotte group, resulting in a dense forest growth, which provides their chief industry.

Graham Island, largest of the group, may also be compared with Prince Edward Island, than which it is slightly larger. The former has over five billion feet of timber, while Prince Edward has none. Graham contains about 1,300 square miles of fairly level land—the rest mountainous,—much of which after clearing and draining is capable of producing good crops, while Prince Edward is nearly all arable land. Gold, silver, copper, and coal are found on Graham Island, and its underlying sedimentary rocks show evidences of oil, while Prince Edward Island has none of these.

Most of the present agricultural development on Graham Island is near the coast. An experimental farm at Lawn Hill has demonstrated that Indian corn and tomatoes, as well as the general run of field and garden vegetables do well, and two crops of strawberries can be harvested in a season. Lack of market is the principal reason why more farming is not done, although the cost of either clearing the timbered land or preparing the peaty soil in other parts is a further obstacle. As in other new regions, this should be done as part of an extensive planned project which, however, will not be feasible until there is a better market for farm produce than now exists.

Moresby Island, next in size to Graham, with an area of 967 square miles, is even more heavily timbered, a characteristic shared by most of the smaller islands in the group.

The Queen Charlotte Islands have a mild climate, if perhaps somewhat wet, and should some day provide homes for a large and varied population. At present, however, they mean little to most Canadians, including the people of British Columbia, who would find it hard to recall the names of more than one or two of them.

Vancouver, at the southern extremity of the British

Columbia coast, is now Canada's third city in size, containing more than one third of the people of the province. Books have been written about Vancouver, and also about Victoria, and most people who know anything at all about British Columbia know something about this part of the Province In fact, as already mentioned, many people think that the whole of British Columbia has the climatic and other characteristics peculiar to the lower coast region.

For that reason, I shall say no more about Vancouver and the populous region in its vicinity, and shall devote the rest of this chapter to a description of the section of coast farther north, too long neglected, but which some day will help to make British Columbia the great Province it is undoubtedly destined to become. The principal seaport for this region is Prince Rupert, already mentioned more than once. As has been said, part of the Grand Trunk Pacific scheme devised in 1903 was the decision to build a new port near the northwestern extremity of the British Columbia coast. The site selected is on Kaien Island, eight miles long, lying in a well-sheltered spot, a short distance north of the Skeena's mouth, and about 40 miles south of where the Alaska Panhandle cuts British Columbia off from the sea.

Previously, the Skeena River, from Port Essington, near its mouth, to Hazelton, 175 miles upstream, had been navigated by sternwheel river boats which were taken off after the railway came. A few small communities chiefly built around salmon canneries had been in existence, but none of these was chosen as the new terminus. Probably the chief argument in favor of the site finally selected for Prince Rupert was that no one else had got there first, a consideration of prime importance to railway promoters intent upon the sale of town lots, and one that has caused railways all over the West to play tag with established communities. In this instance, Prince Rupert was chopped out of the wilderness, streets were laid out—in some cases, blasted out,—docks were built, a 1,250,000-bushel elevator, and a shipbuilding plant and floating dry-dock were constructed. Then the Grand Trunk Pacific Railway was unable to meet its obligations; the government took over, and everyone but the hardy few who had been induced to make their homes in Prince Rupert and were prepared to stick to the end forgot all about the great new city of the gaudy real estate posters, built to capture the oriental trade and help develop the rich timber, mineral, and agricultural lands of the interior.

Until the second world war, the costly shipbuilding plant and dry-dock were unused; but during the war thirteen 10,000-ton and two 1,500-ton ships and four minesweepers were built there, while over 400 ships visited the dry-dock for repairs. Many thousands of American soldiers and many hundreds of thousands of tons of supplies passed through Prince Rupert for points in Alaska. Since the end of the war, however, United States shipping regulations again operate as before the war to the disadvantage of Prince Rupert. Were it not for these, goods from the middle-western and eastern States might go by rail to Prince Rupert rather than to Seattle, which is two days' sail farther from Alaska. Prince Rupert should not, of course, be compelled to depend upon the vagaries of United States traffic; it could play a much more important part in promoting Canadian trade.

In fact, it now seems probable that Prince Rupert and the rest of this northern coastal strip of British Columbia are soon to come in for an era of development that will make up in a measure for the many years of neglect. One reason for this, of course, is the number of places which almost anywhere else in the world would long since have become important seaports. For example, if any one of hundreds of these inlets existed in the long stretch of coast between the mouth of the Columbia and San Francisco Bay, it could not fail to become a busy seaport and the centre for the adjoining territory, but along the British Columbia coast, where harbour jostles harbour no particular one stands out, especially since the country on all sides is undeveloped.

The chief resources of this coast region are its fisheries, its waterpower, its timber, and its minerals, not necessarily mentioned in order of importance. At present, the largest pulp and paper mill in Canada is established at Ocean Falls, about 200 miles south of Prince Rupert. Dozens of other suitable locations exist, however, should the market for newsprint justify plants being built. Since the end of the war, Columbia Cellulose Company, subsidiary of Celanese Corporation, has built a 250-ton pulp mill on Watson Island, nine miles east of Prince Rupert.

Sawmills, where ocean-going ships can load directly from the mill-dock, and timber can be secured almost at the backdoor, are established at many places on the mainland coast and on the islands, while innumerable suitable sites exist for other mills. The forests in the neighbourhood of Prince Rupert contain about 50 billion feet of merchantable timber, the most important species of which are spruce and hemlock. Cottonwoods grow to large size in some of the valleys, logs from which are now shipped to a veneer plant at New Westminster, but if plants existed locally much larger quantities of this type of timber could be put to use. Cedar poles and piles are now shipped from a number of points along the Skeena.

Salmon-canning was the first industry to become established in this region. It is a characteristic of the salmon that when its time comes to spawn it tries to return from its sojourn in salt water to the spawning-ground where it began life. All the streams that flow into the Pacific contain such spawning-grounds in greater or less degree, and consequently each year receive their quota of yearning fish. Fishermen catch them at estuaries of the rivers and there the canneries are usually located. With proper conservation, this industry should continue indefinitely, but it is not likely ever to be an expanding one. The halibut fisheries, on the other hand, may be expanded somewhat. In the waters surrounding Queen Charlotte Islands, and in Queen Charlotte Sound, to the south

140

of the archipelago, where submerged mountains provide feeding grounds, immense quantities of halibut can be taken, so far without any apparent danger of serious depletion. Prince Rupert is now the world's largest fresh-halibut source, and has a cold-storage plant in which it is possible to walk for what seems miles between stacks of frozen fish. Most of the fish is shipped from Prince Rupert in the frozen state, but there is also a possibility that fish-processing plants might be established there.

The area adjacent to the town of Stewart, at the head of Portland Canal, which forms the southeastern boundary between British Columbia and the Alaska Panhandle, is highly mineralized, and gold and copper mines are already in operation there, while another important mining region has been partly developed at the head of Alice Arm, an extension of Observatory Inlet. This region lies north of Prince Rupert, but many other mining regions quite as favourable, geologically, await development farther south as the difficulties of prospecting are overcome. In addition to this, the country about the headwaters of the Skeena, and farther north in Cassiar, is also well mineralized. Some mines in the vicinity of Hazelton are being operated, while many others await better transportation. As already mentioned, an extensive field of anthracite and low-volatile bituminous coal is located in the Groundhog basin, northeast of Hazelton. These inland mineral resources are really part of the region described in the previous chapter, but they are also tributary to Prince Rupert, whose future is to a certain extent bound up with them.

Probably the most important resource of the region under review is its waterpower. While the streams that rise in the Coast Mountains and empty into the Pacific are short, their channels are often steep, and in consequence provide many waterpower sites. The most important development proposed for this region, however, is concerned with water that flows in the opposite direction, eventually reaching the Pacific by way of the Fraser, many hundreds of miles to the south.

The Nechako River, which empties into the Fraser at Prince George, drains a group of dazzlingly beautiful lakes nestling among the foothills of the Coast Mountains. These lakes, the principal ones of which are seven in number, all long, narrow and irregular of outline, with their connecting streams constitute what is called the "Great Circle" water route, about 200 miles around a pear-shaped circuit, and comprising about 1,300 square miles.

The Aluminum Company of Canada Limited, has secured power rights in this area and proposes to dam the Nechako a short distance below its source in Lake Natalkuz, the easternmost of the group. Then, by a tunnel ten miles long and 36 feet in diameter, or possibly two tunnels of 28-foot diameter, bored through the mountains to the west, the great reservoir will be tapped from Lake Tahtsa, the northwestern-most of the lakes, and the water carried to a powerhouse to be built on the Kemano River, which flows from the western slope of the mountains. From the powerhouse, the power will go over transmission lines to the aluminum plant and other plants to be built at the head of Kitimat Arm, an extension of Douglas Channel, reaching inland from the coast, a distance of about 100 miles. This channel is navigable for ocean-going ships which will bring the bauxite from British Guiana, by way of the Panama Canal. In addition to communication by sea, plans call for a branch from the CNR's Prince Rupert line.

Thus the Aluminum Company of Canada proposes, on the Pacific coast, to duplicate its great power and aluminium plants now turning out aluminum ingots on the Saguenay. The B. C. project is expected to involve the investment of upwards of $500 million, and will require many years to complete. Surveys begun in 1949 have been conducted chiefly to test footings for the dam, which will be 200 feet high, and to check estimates concerning the great reservoir. Some idea of the size of this reservoir, which will be 120 miles

Fishing Fleet, Prince Rupert, B

long, may be obtained from the engineers' estimate, that eight years will be required for the water to reach its top level, about 170 feet above the present low level.

While the proposed development is within the limits of Tweedsmuir Park, in an area of extreme beauty, it should be possible to make use of this immense waterpower, and at the same time not despoil the beauty of the region. The present channels of connecting streams will be drowned out, of course, and the lakes themselves will be swollen much beyond their original proportions, but they will still be surrounded by beautiful mountains rising from the water's edge, some of which reach heights of almost 7,000 feet above the sea. The level of the highest lakes at present is about 2,850 feet. Consequently, if proper care be taken to see that the beauty of the region does not suffer, the fact that it is contributing so greatly to the material welfare of the country might even add to the joy which successive generations may receive from the deep, clear lakes and the perpetually snow-capped mountains mirrored in their crystal depths.

Since, except for a few Indians, the territory in which this great undertaking is being developed is practically uninhabited, and since a city will be needed to operate the plants made possible by such a supply of power, one of the most important features of the scheme will be the planning of such a city, for which a fine site exists at Kitimat. In this the Aluminum Company has the advantage of experience gained in the planning of its town of Arvida, on the Saguenay. At Arvida, while many of its citizens hail from elsewhere, many others were drawn from the surrounding country, which had been settled for more than 100 years, but at Kitimat it will be necessary to import everyone. Since, however, the project will take many years to complete, the people can be brought in gradually as their labour is required. Nevertheless, it will be a considerable undertaking, and will provide an excellent opportunity to work out principles of town-planning from the very beginning.

p and Paper Plant, Ocean Falls, B.C.

Because the mountains border the sea with practically no coastal plain, agricultural possibilities are generally limited, except where rivers have cut wide valleys, bringing down silt to deposit in their lower reaches. The Skeena, although it has cut a narrow channel through the mountains, towards its mouth occupies a valley about two miles wide. Immediately east of the mountains, the valley widens from its previous narrow confines, and other wide valleys open off, all of which contain good agricultural land. The Nass River Valley, roughly paralleling the Skeena, a few miles to the north, also contains areas of agricultural land; and a considerable extent of territory, reaching northward to the Stikine Valley, is suited to stockraising.

Despite the lack of large continuous stretches of arable land, many relatively small areas are to be found in some of the valleys and on some of the islands which, because of other factors, may some day provide homes for many people. Chief of these other factors is the sea. By means of irregular arms and inlets, many of which are connected with each other, the sea frequently finds its way far inland. An example is Douglas Channel, running northward and then northeastward to Kitimat Arm, at the top of which the proposed aluminum plant is to be located. Parallel to Douglas Channel, on the east, and separated from it by mountainous Hawkesbury and Gribbell Islands, are Ursula and Devastation channels which join Douglas Channel where Kitimat Arm begins. Then, opening out of the eastern side of Devastation Channel, Gardner Canal extends southeastward for about 100 miles. This maze of tortuous inland sea channels comprises about 350 miles of deep-water navigation, surrounded by territory rich in minerals, timber, waterpower, and fisheries.

Another region, farther south, somewhat similar in physiography, consists of Dean and Burke channels, separated from each other by King Island and connected beyond the latter by Labouchere Channel. The double-pronged North and South Bentinck Arms extend eastward from the junction of

Labouchere and Burke channels. Ocean Falls is on Fisher
Channel, near the entrance to Dean Channel; while the town
of Bella Coola, where Alexander Mackenzie reached the
Pacific in 1793, is at the top of North Bentinck Arm. As with
the Douglas Channel-Gardner Canal section, this widespreading area, with its tentacle-like inlets, must certainly
some day become famous for the homesites of extreme beauty
that it offers. Incidentally, Captain George Voncouver,
who surveyed most of this coast in 1793, is responsible for
the preponderance of English names which these inlets and
other marine features bear. As Mackenzie made his gruelling
journey across the interior uplands, Vancouver, in boats, was
carefully surveying the coast. Neither of these two great men
who left their names on the map of Canada knew of the
other's presence.

The coast region of British Columbia here described is
another in which scenery will always be a leading asset. For
many years, the Inside Passage has attracted its share of
summer tourists, many of whom continue on to the Yukon
and Alaska, while others leave the ship at Prince Rupert to
make the Triangle Tour by rail to Red Pass Junction, on the
western flank of the Rockies, thence by way of the CNR
mainline down the North Thompson to Kamloops, and back
to Vancouver. When the PGE is completed to Prince George,
an alternative route to Vancouver will be provided, making
available an opportunity for tourists to see what in many
respects is the most striking scenery of all.

At present, ships sailing the Inside Passage pass by
hundreds of beautiful inlets suitable for pleasure resorts,
where mountain-climbing, fishing, and boating could offer
inducements in summer, with skiing and other seasonable
sports in winter. Naturally, this industry will require time
to become established, but once that is done it should be an
asset for all time, since the nature of the country will not
alter, nor the need for recreation grow less.

Thus, with its many possible harbours, this region is

capable of providing opportunities for a large industrial population, either in developing its resources, or in applying power produced locally to raw materials brought by sea. In addition to this, it could provide recreational facilities not only for its own people, but for others from all parts of the world.

13

The Final Frontier

A S we have seen, except in a few scattered spots in the interior of British Columbia, that distinctive symbol of North America, the western frontier, has disappeared. Although Canadians have not tended to glamourize it as their neighbours to the south have done, the western frontier was common to both; but the greater part of the new frontier, stretching across the North from the Atlantic to Bering sea, belongs to Canada. A broad northern zone is about to be incorporated into the better-settled parts of the country, but the frontier will remain: it will merely have been pushed farther north. Except for the Mackenzie Valley, part of the more southerly zone, the final frontier will extend in Canada from the Atlantic to the boundary between Yukon and Alaska; and from there it will continue across Alaska for a further 750 miles. The area embraced by the frontier in Canada comprises Yukon Territory, the greater part of the District of Mackenzie, all of the districts of Keewatin and Franklin and the northern tip of Quebec, called the Ungava Peninsula. Aside from two peninsulas protruding from the mainland just west of Hudson Bay, the District of Franklin consists of arctic islands, some among the largest in the world.

Yukon Territory, comprising 207,076 of the million and a half square miles comprised in this final frontier, lies west of the Mackenzie and Richardson mountains, and north of the 60th parallel, which divides it from British Columbia to the south. For a brief period, it held the world's spotlight. In 1896, placer gold, similar to that found in Cariboo in the sixties, was discovered on a number of streams flowing into the Yukon River. One of these, called the Klondike, gave its name to the gold rush which, at its height, brought upwards of 30,000 people to Yukon Territory. Dawson, on the east bank of the Yukon River, a few miles below the mouth of the Klondike, was the centre of the boom. The stampeders, drawn from all over the world, came by various routes, chief of which was by ship to Skagway, at the top of the Alaska Panhandle, thence, on foot, over the famous Chilkoot Pass to Lake Bennett, source of the Lewes River, one of the Yukon's principal tributaries, where canoes, boats, and barges of all descriptions were built. In these, the gold-seekers floated downstream to Dawson, a distance of 600 miles. Only one serious obstruction existed—at Miles Canyon, just above Whitehorse, 460 miles from Dawson. As soon as they could be built, steamers were in operation both above and below Whitehorse.

After 1900, travellers went by rail from Skagway to White-horse over the White Pass & Yukon Railway, a narrow-gauge line, 111 miles long. This railway, in its short length, passes from Alaska, through British Columbia, into Yukon Territory. Built to serve the Klondike goldfields, one of its main sup-. ports now is tourists, since it can offer more thrills for its length than almost any other railway on the continent. In addition to those who came by Skagway, many travelled by steamer up-river from St. Michael, at the mouth of the Yukon. The distance was great (1,600) miles) and the time required was long, since the river has a strong, steady current and its channels shift so quickly that even an experienced pilot would frequently find his boat aground.

Few gold-booms have ever equalled the Klondike in its heyday, and its essence and flavour have been preserved in the poems of Robert Service. Dan McGrew and Sam McGee lived only in Service's imagination, but to many they are much more real than Skagway's Soapy Smith, who did live— for a while. The time came, however, as in California and Cariboo, when the richest ground was worked out and new creeks became few and far between. Dawson, at its peak a rip-roaring, rollicking city of about 25,000, declined in a few years to less than 1,000. Ground that had been rifled of its richest stores when there was not time to search the crannies or sift the lean sands and gravels for less profitable offerings, was now worked over by giant hydraulics and dredgers, and this could only be done on a large scale by companies with capital to install expensive equipment. This type of mining still continues, and the Klondike is no longer a "poor man's camp."

Physiographically, Yukon Territory is a northward extension of British Columbia. The Mackenzie and Richardson mountains, like the Rockies, of which they are a continuation, consist chiefly of sedimentary rocks. To the west, the Pelly, Selwyn and Ogilvie mountains rise from high uplands, similar to others in the interior of British Columbia, and, like the latter, consist of both sedimentary and granitic rocks. Then, in the southwestern corner, the St. Elias Mountains, culminating in Mount Logan, 19,850 feet high, are, like the Coast Mountains to the south, chiefly of granitic rocks.

The Yukon River, one branch of which rises in the flanks of the St. Elias Mountains, and another in the flanks of the Mackenzie Mountains, flows northwestward through the central Yukon Plateau and crosses into Alaska, which it more or less bisects on its way to Bering Sea. It is a mighty river which, including its many large tributaries, is navigable for a total of 3,500 miles.

Despite its northerly position, there are many sections of Yukon Territory, especially in the south-central valleys, where oats, wheat, and barley, as well as most kinds of garden and field vegetables, can be grown. Since 1917, the Government of Canada has maintained an experimental sub-station near Dawson, where plot tests have produced wheat and barley running to 60 bushels, and oats to 134 bushels an acre. Wheat planted on a farm in the Yukon Valley has been harvested in 87 days. The most likely spot for future agricultural development is in the Takhini-Dezadeash valleys, west of Whitehorse, where a combined valley from three to four miles wide extends for about 100 miles. The land here is level and gently sloping, lightly covered in places with timber, and in other places consisting of open, grassy areas, while the soil is similar in appearance to the dark-brown prairie soils. Nevertheless, Yukon Territory is not primarily an agricultural region.

Its two principal resources are minerals and timber. Very rich silver-lead ore is mined in the Mayo District, about 180 miles up the Stewart River, one of the large tributaries of the Yukon. Ore from mines on Keno Hill in this region has been shipped since 1913 to smelters in the United States or British Columbia, but, of course, only the richest ore would justify the transportation costs, and in 1941 mining operations on Keno Hill were discontinued.

In 1945, however, a new era began for Keno Hill. In that year a group of Toronto mining men, headed by Fred M. Connell, acquired control of the principal properties, since operated by a company called United Keno Hill Mines Limited. Ample capital was provided and a vigorous development program undertaken which has shown the property to be an exceptionally valuable one. This situation was improved by the completion of a 247-mile highway, connecting Mayo with the Alaska Highway near Whitehorse and by the announcement that the Government of Canada will develop a hydro project on the Mayo River which will ultimately produce 8,000 horsepower. The highway will enable ore to be shipped all through the year, while the advent of hydro-electric power will considerably reduce mining and concentration costs.

Several other companies, attracted by the success of United Keno Hill, have begun development of adjoining properties, and the prospect now is that the Mayo camp may develop into one of the leading silver-lead mining camps of

Part of B.C.'s "Sea of Mountai

Siberia

Alaska

Fairbanks

Porcupine R.

Yukon R.

Dawson

Whitehorse

Peel R.

Norman W

Mackenzie

ASIA

ALASKA HIGHWAY

Liard R.

Fort Nelson

TO

ROAD

Dawson Creek
Grimshaw

Peace R.

Peace River

Canada

Athabaska R.

waterways

Seattle

Edmonton

U.S.A.

North America, with a smelter as a possibility of the near future.

Next to the Mayo District the most important at present is that in the vicinity of Whitehorse where gold, silver, copper, lead, zinc, antimony, manganese, molybdenite, tungsten, and several other minerals have been found in varying quantities. Lack of large proven deposits and distance from market has held back development, but recently companies like Noranda and Hudson Bay Mining and Smelting have done considerable exploratory work in the area, with the possibility that more profitable ore-bodies may be discovered.

What may be of even greater importance is the discovery reported to the Geological Survey of Canada by Dr. H. S. Bostock of huge deposits of high grade hematite iron ore near the head of Bonnet Plume River, a tributary of the Peel. The deposits extend southeastward from the Alaskan boundary, forming an arc about 550 miles in length. The iron formations have been traced by air, in the vicinity of the head of Bonnet Plume River, for about 130 miles.

One estimate of available Yukon coal in seams more than three feet thick is 231,160,000 tons.

The District of Mackenzie, consisting of more than half a million square miles, occupies the area between Yukon Territory, on the west, and the District of Keewatin, on the east. That it contains Canada's largest river and the two largest lakes wholly within Canada, might seem to be distinction enough, but it also contains the Yellowknife goldfields and the uranium-producing deposits of Great Bear Lake.

Parallel to the Districts' western boundary, the Mackenzie River flows for a thousand miles, from its source in Great Slave Lake to Arctic tidewater, receiving midway of its course the discharge of Great Bear Lake, 90 miles to the east. Slave River, draining Lake Athabaska, and taking in the Peace, is really an upper section of the Mackenzie.

At Fort Smith, just within Mackenzie District, the Slave

drops over a gneissic spur of the Canadian Shield, and in a 16-mile series of heavy rapids descends a total of 125 feet. Since the Slave is a mighty stream, the power possibilities of this great cataract are considerable. The Taltson and Snowdrift rivers, following somewhat parallel courses to the east, are both capable of providing power at a number of places, while the possibilities of the Lockhart system have already been described. Additional power could be derived from Camsell River, with its line of lakes stretching almost from Great Slave Lake to Great Bear.

Therefore, with the oil resources already mentioned, and this potential waterpower, the western part of Mackenzie District is a natural extension of the industrial region farther south, already described, especially if, as suggested later, the Road to Asia should become a reality. The edge of the Canadian Shield cuts about midway through Great Slave and Great Bear Lakes; the height of land separating the Hudson Bay and Mackenzie watersheds runs not far from the eastern end of these lakes, and consequently streams flowing westward are mostly short and greatly broken by waterfalls.

Most of Mackenzie District west of the height of land is forested, with some fairly large timber in the Mackenzie Valley, but in the Shield section the timber is suitable only for pulp, if, in many places, its small size and relative inaccessibility would permit of its being so used.

Keewatin District, little more than half the size of Mackenzie, occupies that part of the mainland east of Mackenzie District, extending to Hudson Bay. It consists almost entirely of Precambrian rocks, generally in massive formation, and only in certain places subjected to the disturbances which have occurred in many other parts of the Shield. These rocks dip beneath overlying sedimentary formations as the Hudson Bay shore is approached, and in places along the coast the latter are intruded by crystalline schists, lavas and quartzites.

The Hudson Bay watershed, unlike that draining into the

Mackenzie, slopes gradually since the distance is much greater. The principal streams in this region are the Thelon, Dubawnt, its chief tributary, and the Kazan, all of which rise in Mackenzie District and flow across Keewatin, their waters eventually reaching Hudson Bay. Back River, farther north, follows a similar course, but fails to reach Hudson Bay, discharging into the Arctic instead.

The principal geographic feature of Keewatin District is the Thelon River, which crosses it from west to east. Its main branch heads not far from the eastern end of Great Slave Lake, while the Dubawnt heads close to the eastern end of Lake Athabaska. The two unite near the boundary between Mackenzie and Keewatin districts and the combined stream flows eastward into Baker Lake, which leads directly into Chesterfield Inlet, an arm of Hudson Bay. By means of Chesterfield Inlet and Baker Lake, fairly large ships can sail 200 miles inland, while the Thelon River provides a water route for small boats over the greater part of the distance between Baker and Great Slave Lakes. This waterway will always be associated with the names of J. W. and J. B. Tyrrell, who, in 1893, made the first exploratory journey from Lake Athabaska to Hudson Bay along the Dubawnt and Thelon rivers. An account of this journey was written by J. W. Tyrrell in his book, *Across the Sub-Arctics of Canada*, which has become a classic of Canadian exploration,

Except for Boothia and Melville peninsulas, the District of Franklin consists of islands, among them, as has been said, some of the largest in the world. It is safe to say that few Canadians have a very clear picture of this part of Canada, although it comprises more than half a million square miles. While the total number of islands runs into many hundreds (two new ones aggregating over 5,000 square miles were discovered from the air in 1948), the more important ones can be reduced to fifteen. These can be divided into two groups, a northern one and a southern one, separated by the broad, continuous passage formed by Lancaster Sound, Barrow Strait, Melville Sound, and McClure Strait, which extends across the archipelago from east to west. This passage does not provide a reliable route for ships because parts of it are blocked each season by ice; but in 1944 the Royal Canadian Mounted Police schooner *St. Roch,* Sergeant (now Inspector) Henry Larsen in command, sailed from Pond Inlet, Baffin Island, on August 17, passed along Lancaster Sound, through Barrow Strait into Melville Sound, and then turned south through Prince of Wales Strait, which separates Victoria and Banks Islands, reaching the R.C.M.P. post at Holman Island, off the west coast of Victoria Island, on September 4, thus making the famed Northwest Passage in only 18 days!

The southern group of seven contains the two largest in the archipelago, Baffin and Victoria (201,600 and 80,450 square miles, respectively), the former of which is nearly two and a half times the size of the Island of Great Britain. The southeastern coast of Baffin Island constitutes the northern shore of Hudson Strait, while its northeastern coast lies parallel to Greenland, from which it is separated by Davis Strait and Baffin Bay. As it sprawls northwestward across 30 degrees of longitude, it forms a jaunty sort of cap for Hudson Bay. Victoria Island, slightly longer east and west than it is broad, lies due north of Alberta and Saskatchewan (with the districts of Mackenzie and Keewatin in between), while, to the west, is Banks Island, (25,992 square miles, almost as large as New Brunswick). Somerset Island (9,540 square miles), Prince of Wales Island (14,004 square miles), and the much smaller King William Island (5,108 square miles), where the survivors of Franklin's wrecked ships died in 1847, with Melville and Boothia peninsulas, occupy the space between Baffin and Victoria islands. Southampton Island (16,936 square miles) is in Hudson Bay, opposite the western end of Hudson Strait.

In the northern group of eight, Ellesmere Island (75,024

square miles), lying in a generally north and south direction, 485 miles in length with an average width of 150 miles, is the largest. Only a narrow channel separates it from the northwestern tip of Greenland and its most northerly point, the northernmost in Canada, is within seven degrees of the Pole. Immediately to the west, lies Axel Heiberg Island (13,248 square miles) and to the south, Devon Island (20,-484 square miles). To the west of Axel Heiberg, are Ellef Rignes (3,719 square miles), North Borden (1,300 square miles), and South Borden (2,100 square miles); south of these, but still north of McClure Strait, are Bathurst (7,000 square miles), Melville (16,164 square miles), and Prince Patrick (7,192 square miles). The preponderance of English names indicates the great interest which for over 300 years English navigators maintained in the search for the Northwest Passage. The few Norse names result from the explorations of Otto Sverdrup in 1899-1902, while the Borden Islands were discovered by Stefansson in 1916.

The eastern coast of Baffin Island and parts of the interior are high and rugged, glacier-covered mountains rising in places to over 5,000 feet. High land also exists in Devon and Ellesmere islands, reaching elevations of 10,000 feet in the latter; and here, too, is much permanent ice. Baffin Island is largely an extension of the Precambrian Shield. Generally, the islands in the eastern part of the archipelago are high, while those farther west are much lower, consisting chiefly of sedimentary rocks. The lower land, even some of the most northerly, is well covered with Arctic vegetation and supports herds of caribou and musk-oxen, or ovibos, as Stefansson prefers to call them.

Despite the fact that the broad zone discussed in previous chapters has been rescued from the great wasteland of former times, some might think that this northerly million and a half square miles must surely remain largely a wasteland, but even it cannot be so written off. Although most of this region may never produce much in the way of crops, it could produce large quantities of livestock. This would not be cattle or sheep, of course, but reindeer and musk-oxen, which are at home there, and once grazed in immense herds. But before we proceed to discuss this possibility, some misapprehensions concerning the nature of the country must be dispelled. Yukon Territory is mountainous, and also has considerable areas of rolling upland, which formerly provided pasturage for large herds of caribou. The Mackenzie and Richardson mountains provide no pasturage at all; but in the whole territory between the eastern foothills and the mountains that fringe the eastern shores of Baffin Island and Labrador, the land is relatively low and fairly level. Most of the area is without trees, but more or less thickly carpeted with grasses and mosses, depending more on the nature of the soil than upon any other factor. Many shrubs grow, but mostly they keep their heads down, creeping close to the ground, or clustering in gullies.

The governing factor in connection with vegetation-growth is the length of the summer days, which to a large extent offset the lateness of spring and the shortness of summer. Plants hold their seeds during the winter, and drop them in the early summer on the moist earth that is warmed by almost constant sunlight; they are thus favourably placed for quick germination and growth, and the effect is amazing. The first few days of spring effect a surprising change, converting the drab winter shades to vivid green, and many-hued flowers follow in rapid succession. Summer reaches its height in July, when the landscape is a riot of bloom. Summer winds are usually moderate, and gales are of short duration. According to standards elsewhere, precipitation is scanty, but plants have a perpetual source of moisture in the permanently frozen subsoil (permafrost), just below their roots. Early in August, as plants mature, the green of summer quickly merges into the tints of autumn, and winds become stronger and more keen. By the end of August, or early September, colour is again the dominant note, as the frosts of coming winter cause the trailing willows to take on their bright yellow hues, and other shrubbery goes in for purple and reds.

Contrary to popular belief, the snowfall in the far north is not heavy; most of the snow that falls remains throughout the winter, but it drifts into the lee of hills or into gullies, so that on level land, where the wind gets a fair sweep, little snow remains, allowing the vegetation of the previous summer to be easily secured by grazing animals.

These animals, as already mentioned, are the caribou and the musk-ox. The former was once found all over this northern region, extending southward into parts within the present settled zone, where, in many places, it is still found. Its principal home, however, is the treeless lands of the far north. It belongs to the deer family, larger than most of the common species, though smaller than the elk. Unlike most deer, both sexes have horns, which are large and widespreading. The horns are shed in winter and grow out rapidly again in spring. Caribou have thin, graceful legs and broad hooves, which enable them to walk without sinking in the wet tundra or in snow.

Over large areas of northern Europe and Asia, caribou, called reindeer when domesticated, have been herded by natives since before the dawn of history. This animal has provided the people with meat and milk for food, bones and horns for tools and weapons, and hides for tents and clothing. Not only that, but it serves as a beast of burden, either ridden or hitched to a sleigh. The reindeer, unlike most other domestic animals, does not require its master, in payment for its contribution to his welfare, to labour in the hayfield, but forages for itself, both summer and winter.

The Eskimos and Indians of North America never tamed the caribou, preferring to hunt it as a wild animal. This was fairly satisfactory so long as they used only the bow and arrow or the spear. Caribou could hold their own against such weapons; but when white men arrived with firearms, the situation quickly changed. The natives, never thinking of tomorrow's need, and, indeed, never doubting that the supply of game was inexhaustible, slaughtered the caribou with fine abandon. The dire effects of this were first felt in Alaska, where contact with whites and their destructive weapons was of longest duration; and, in the 1890s caribou became so scarce in many places that the Eskimos were on the verge of starvation. Yet, across narrow Bering Strait, Eskimos similar in culture lived in relative comfort because they were reindeer-herders, killing for food only animals in excess of breeding requirements.

In this emergency an enterprising missionary named Sheldon Jackson raised money in the United States and began to import reindeer from Siberia. In the first year—1892—he brought over only 16 head; the next year, 167 head, and so on, until 1902, when the Russian government withdrew its permit. The total number brought in during the ten years was 1,280. These were divided among the Eskimos with the stipulation that only excess males should be killed for food and that females should not be sold to non-Eskimos. This was to keep the deer in Eskimo hands. The United States Bureau of Education, in charge of the scheme, brought in Laplanders to teach the natives the rudiments of animal husbandry, and the Lapps were paid partly in reindeer, including females. In this way large herds eventually grew up over which the Bureau had no control, some of which were bought by Lomen Brothers, of Nome, who soon became the owners of considerable herds, the increment of which they slaughtered for commercial purposes.

The time inevitably came when Canadian Eskimos found themselves approaching the point that the Alaskan Eskimos had reached in the 1890s; and the Government of Canada bought a herd of reindeer from Lomen Brothers to be delivered on the east bank of the Mackenzie, near its mouth. The drive from Seward Peninsula, across the northern parts of Alaska and Yukon Territories to the Mackenzie River took five years; and in the spring of 1935 the herd, numbering

2,370 head, reached the special grazing-grounds selected, about 50 miles northeast of Aklavik. They have increased rapidly in their new home, and are being distributed to Eskimos in somewhat the same manner as was originally done in Alaska. The Northwest Territories Administration is supervising the scheme, and undertakes the training of Eskimo herders.

This is all very well as far as it goes, but reindeer could play a much more important rôle than that. There is no reason why the vast unoccupied tundras should not eventually become stocked with them, not tended and herded, as in the past, by men on foot, but by modern methods. This, like growing trees, is a long-range project, not likely to attract those who wish to realize a quick profit, and should therefore be undertaken as a national enterprise. As the world's range-lands are more and more given over to the plough, the need for pasturage will become greater; but the tundras of the North will never be so requisitioned. Reindeer multiply rapidly; and, even starting in a small way, the time could come when the best grazing-grounds were completely stocked. The man on foot with a dog should, of course, be superseded by men in helicopters; corrals should be built at strategic places, with abattoirs and cold-storage plants within easy reach of transportation.

The other meat animal native to the North is the musk-ox, which once roamed the continent as far south as Kentucky, but is now confined chiefly to the northern parts of Mackenzie and Keewatin districts and to some of the islands of the Arctic archipelago. Like the caribou, it needs no one to build barns or cut hay for it, but grazes both summer and winter on tundra vegetation. As its scientific name, *ovibos moschatus*, implies, it resembles both a cow and a sheep; its flesh and milk are similar to those of cattle, while its long wool can be made into lovely, soft garments. This animal has never been domesticated, and where kept in zoos often shows a cranky disposition; but there is little doubt that if a serious attempt were made to domesticate, and by selective breeding improve it, a very valuable meat- and wool-producing animal would be the result.

This is a project that should be of particular interest to Canadians, since, except for a few in Greenland, all the musk-oxen in the world are in Canada, and none too many at that. They are now protected by law, and it is possible that their extinction, once quite imminent, may be prevented; but negative action of this sort is not enough. Aside from the turkey, no domestic animal or bird has been tamed since before the beginning of history, and Canadians now have the unique chance to share with prehistoric man the thrill of taming a new animal.

The mineral possibilities of the Precambrian rocks of the Shield have been referred to frequently in this book, and it can be assumed that in this most northerly zone they will not fail to contribute their share of minerals. The islands, however, vary in their geology, most of the western ones consisting largely of sedimentary rocks. Even with the little prospecting that has been done, coal of good quality has been discovered on Banks, Melville, Axel Heiberg, and Ellesmere islands, as well as on many of the smaller ones. While only the drill can finally determine the presence of oil, favourable indications exist in many of the islands, which would suggest that some day Franklin District may very well add its quota to Canada's oil supplies. Furthermore, since neither coal nor oil can ever be produced from the Precambrian rocks of the northern mainland, the presence of either on nearby islands would undoubtedly prove of great value in the development, for example, of the extensive copper occurrences known to exist between Bathurst Inlet and the Coppermine River.

While we are dealing with Arctic resources, we should not overlook one of the most important—the Eskimos. As usually happens when a simpler culture comes in contact with civilization, the primitive people get the worst of it. Such is certainly the case with the Eskimos; and if and when the North is opened up, the Eskimos, unable to maintain their way of life, and poorly equipped to adjust to those aspects of civilization with which they come in contact, must sooner or later be exterminated. This would be a great crime; yet, unless something is done very soon there can be no other result. Present facilities for the education of Eskimos not only unfit them for continuing with their previous mode of life, but fail to fit them for any other.

These people, the product of countless generations of rigorous natural selection, are, in the main, a highly-intelligent race. As has been said, their primitive way of life, even if it were desirable, will not much longer be possible, and they must therefore be fitted with an alternative. While every Canadian child should have the best possible opportunity to secure an education that will enable him to get the most out of life, these descendants of Canada's first people, now so few in number, might be dealt with specially. It is hard to think of any project which the people of Canada could undertake that holds more intriguing prospects. Who can say that from among them may not come some of the future leaders in Government or industry, in the arts or sciences? No one who knows these splendid people will think this at all fantastic.

Thus, at last, Canada's area could all be utilized, and the wasteland myth relegated to the place where all myths belong. The Last Frontier, like every other, will some day be conquered; and it will then be found that with its many and varied resources, human included, Canada's most northerly lands can make a contribution to the common welfare proportionately equal to that of any other region. Here, then, is another challenge to Canada during this, her own century!

14

Road to Asia

THE next war, if and when it comes, may find the United States on one side and the Soviet Union on the other, with Canada as one of the chief battlefields. To prevent such a catastrophe should be the aim of everyone. Although Soviet Asia and America almost touch at Bering Strait, their peoples are oceans apart in understanding; yet when they waged a common war the bond between them was strong. To recapture and continue something of that accord is the one great hope of humanity in the days ahead. A move in that direction might be participation in another joint enterprise. Such an enterprise, worthy of the peoples concerned—which also includes Canadians,—might be the re-establishment of the prehistoric highway between the continents at Bering Strait.

As this is written, the tension between the Soviet Union and the western nations is greater than at any time since the end of the second world war, and it may seem fantastic to suggest that they—especially the Soviet Union and the United States,—might co-operate in anything. Nevertheless, the modern world will not admit of a long-continued gulf between East and West; and since some day, even though its dawn may still be shrouded in mists of the future, the project described in this chapter must eventually be undertaken; for that reason it may not be out of place to consider it with that remote possibility in view.

Everything points to Bering Strait as the port of entry for America's first immigrants who arrived, scientists now think, between 25,000 and 30,000 years ago. Bering Strait is only

56 miles across at its narrowest; midway are the two Diomede Islands. Eskimos in their skin boats go back and forth between the two continents without difficulty. It is quite possible that once the land was continuous. Scientists estimate that during the Ice Ages the immense masses of ice which covered a large part of the earth's surface must have caused a lowering of the sea level. Some authorities estimate that in this way the level was lowered by over 250 feet. If this is correct, then not only Bering Strait but a great part of shallow Bering Sea was dry land during the time that the ice was thickest. Geologists are agreed that during the final Ice Age the central Alaskan plain and the region bordering Bering Sea were free of land ice; and so was the depression extending along the eastern slopes of the mountains, leading into the heart of North America.

The findings of archaeologists lend support to the view that the first Americans came by way of Bering Strait, moved up the Yukon Valley, crossed to the Mackenzie, and eventually spread over the whole of the Americas. It might therefore be an appropriate gesture for people on this continent to take the lead in re-establishing the highway between the continents. If this were done, it might mean that anyone who owned a car, living anywhere from the tip of Patagonia to the western extremity of Portugal, could get behind the wheel and roam the greater part of the world under his own power, an interchange of peoples which no Iron Curtain could withstand for very long.

If you look at the map, you will see that the Mackenzie River, flowing out of Great Slave Lake, maintains a generally northwesterly course, cutting across eight degrees of latitude and nearly 20 degrees of longitude. Its mouth is about 13 degrees farther west than the longitude of Vancouver. You will note, too, that passes cross the mountains from the Mackenzie to the Yukon, some of which are no higher than 2,500 feet above the sea. You will note also that the Mackenzie and Yukon rivers provide an almost direct route to Bering Sea from the central and eastern portions of North America. They constitute a natural highway; and since Bering Strait is such a narrow strip of water, with its shores and channel in solid rock, a tunnel between America and Asia would be fairly easy to construct.

Fortunately, it is not necessary to wait until the whole scheme becomes feasible. Americans have desired a railway to Alaska for many years, and this is the logical route for the main line. Mining developments at Great Slave Lake already require a railway, and its extension down the Mackenzie Valley would come as a matter of course. The silver-lead mines in the Mayo District and the recently-discovered iron deposits at the head of Bonnet Plume River, if present expectations are justified, would both require a railway and are tributary to the route suggested here. Railways, highways, and airlines are complementary to one another; once a railway was built, the others would follow. Even now, the highway is at Great Slave Lake. The need of some agency to provide a long-term plan is evident.

It might be objected that this route would duplicate the Alaska Highway and Northwest Staging Route, which now provide highway and air connection between Edmonton and Fairbanks. There would be some duplication, of course, but since the Mackenzie route will in time be developed—for local traffic, if for no other,—the Alaska Highway cannot be considered as an alternative. Although it would have been better had the Mackenzie route been chosen in the first place, the Alaska Highway serves an important section of the country and should by all means be maintained.

How the Alaska Highway route came to be selected in the first place is an interesting story. Previous to the second world war, four routes to Alaska were being actively advanced by different groups of proponents. Two of these traversed the interior of British Columbia, one comparatively close to the coast, the other farther east. The third route, beginning at Edmonton, followed the eastern foothills of the

Rockies northwestward to the break through which the Liard River flows, and then continued up the latter almost to its headwaters, crossing to Whitehorse, and thence to Fairbanks. In passing through the Rockies, in crossing the divide between the Liard and Lewes rivers, the route led over relatively high passes. The fourth route, advocated for many years by Vilhjalmur Stefansson, is the one being suggested here.

Regular airplane service has been available from Edmonton to the Mackenzie delta since 1930, when Canadian Airways Limited began its operations. Shortly after, a competing service was started by Leigh Brintnell of Edmonton, himself an experienced flier. These air-lines maintained regular schedules, both summer and winter, in good weather and in bad; and they, with others who followed them, did more than any other single agency to open up the North. At least up to the outbreak of the second world war, a greater tonnage of freight was carried by air in the Canadian North and Alaska in any one year than in the whole of the United States, outside of Alaska, in the same period. This freight was almost as varied as that handled by any other common carrier — foods of all sorts, furs, fish, gold, mail, mining machinery, cows, horses,—were among the principal items. This was done with a minimum of flying aids. Edmonton has possessed for many years a well-equipped airport, but north of Edmonton there was none that could really be called an airport. Meteorological information left much to be desired, and beam flying was a luxury of which the bush pilot only dreamed. These air services were purely local; flying to Asia was still considered to be in the stunt field, such as the flights of Soviet airmen over the Pole to the United States in 1937.

Nevertheless, there was talk of eventual air routes across the Canadian North. In 1931, partly in the interest of Pan-American Airways, Charles A. Lindbergh had flown from Washington, D. C., across Canada and Alaska to Siberia,

Canada's Century

Japan, and China. The Canadian Government, although doing little at that time to encourage Canadian fliers, was not willing to allow foreign interests to become established in the Canadian aviation field; and, although Lindbergh's flight definitely proved the practicability of the route he pioneered, Pan-American was forced to look elsewhere for a route to the Orient.

In 1937, with an eye to eventual Asian traffic, but with the immediate intention of establishing a claim to the Canadian portion of the route, Grant McConachie, a young Edmonton flier, charted a course through the wilderness from Edmonton to Whitehorse; and on July 5 of that year began a regular weekly mail and passenger service between these points, with a branch service between Fort St. John and Vancouver. At Whitehorse, connection was made with White Pass & Yukon Airways, maintaining regular service between Whitehorse and Dawson, and with Pacific Alaska Airways, a Pan-American subsidiary, operating between Juneau, Fairbanks, and Nome, with a stop at Whitehorse.

McConachie's line, known as Yukon Southern Air Transport, thus supplied the link which provided continuous air communication from the United States and Canada to the edge of Asia. Landing fields existed at Whitehorse and at two intermediate points where small planes could land on wheels during the break-up and freeze-up periods, when neither pontoons nor skis could be used.

Even before the war with Japan began, the Canadian Government had realized the importance of easier communication with Yukon Territory and Alaska; and, since the only established air route was that blazed by McConachie, the Department of Transport proceeded to build airports along the Yukon Southern route, known thereafter as the Northwest Staging Route. Five major airports, about 220 miles apart, were built: at Grande Prairie, Alberta; Fort St. John and Fort Nelson, in British Columbia; and Watson Lake and Whitehorse in Yukon Territory, with six intermediate emer-

166

gency fields. All were equipped with radio beam, and other aids to aerial navigation.

That mountains are in the way is not a serious obstacle to an airline, and the eventual need for a highway to service the airports and for a pipeline in which to transport oil was not envisaged at that time. If what these were to involve had been realized then, it is not likely that the Northwest Staging Route would have followed the course it did. Yet, once the airports were built, the Alaska Highway, along the same route, and eventually the Canol Project, followed inevitably.

After the attack on Pearl Harbour, it was only a matter of weeks before the much-discussed Alaska Highway scheme took definite shape. Conflicting ideas and interests were brushed aside and the decision was reached to build the highway along the route already selected for the Northwest Staging Route. On March 9, 1942, the first unit of the United States Army arrived at Dawson Creek, in that part of British Columbia which lies east of the Rocky Mountains. There was a road of sorts between Dawson Creek and Fort St. John, 50 miles to the north; but between the latter point and Fort Nelson, 275 miles, the track was little better than a trail.

The season was already far gone, but it was vitally important that supplies and equipment for construction be moved from Dawson Creek to Fort Nelson while frost still held the country in its grip. Not only was it necessary to get everything across the broad Peace before the ice went out, but many other streams must be crossed, as well as extensive stretches of muskeg. Long trains drawn by caterpillar tractors hauled the supplies and equipment across the still-frozen countryside, completing the job while everything was firm; and the construction crews were thus able to begin their work with full equipment. Meanwhile, at Whitehorse and Fairbanks, other units were being assembled. Then, simultaneously, units working southeastward from Fairbanks, both ways from Whitehorse and Fort Nelson, and northwestward from Dawson Creek, battled the wilderness.

On September 25, 1942, the unit that had been pushing out from Dawson Creek met the unit working southeastward from Fort Nelson; and exactly a month later, the Negro 97th Regiment, working southeastward from Fairbanks, met the 18th Regiment, pushing northwestward from Whitehorse, and the road was cut through. Although much remained to be done, such as surfacing and bridge-building, a wide, well-built highway of 1,523 miles had been thrown through a wilderness in eight months. The building of the Alaska Highway through such a country in so short a space of time ranks very high as an engineering feat. Its cost would have been unthinkable in peace time; but it shows what can be done when people believe the necessity is great enough.

While this immense effort was directed toward providing highway transportation between the United States and Alaska, a route for a railway was also surveyed, and only the collapse of the Japanese offensive prevented its construction. President Roosevelt's uncle, Warren Delano, who had spent a lifetime building railways, and who hankered to build another, had actually set up his headquarters in Whitehorse preparatory to undertaking personal direction of the railway's construction. Then an unexpected combination of Republicans and southern Democrats in Congress deleted the item covering the cost of the road from the Appropriation Bill, and since the danger of Japanese invasion from that quarter was definitely over, the President was forced to accept the situation and disappoint his uncle. The railway had been planned to connect with the Canadian National Railways at Prince George, B. C., follow the Rocky Mountain Trench northwestward to its intersection with the Liard River—and Alaska Highway,—and then, in a general way, follow the Highway to Fairbanks.

Railway construction was stopped, but the Highway was already built. As a result of the need for speed, major decisions had been made by persons unfamiliar with the country through which the road was to be pushed, not only unfamiliar with long-term implications, but with the short-term ones as well. For no sooner was the Highway completed than it was found necessary to supplement it by a pipeline, 600 miles long, to bring oil across the mountains from the Mackenzie Valley; and, in order to build the pipeline, it was necessary to build supplementary highways in the Mackenzie Valley of greater mileage than the Alaska Highway itself (for winter use only), and a line of temporary airports almost as extensive as the Northwest Staging Route. Therefore, because the Northwest Staging Route was wrongly located in the first place, the Alaska Highway was built at much greater cost in money and labour than would have been necessary; and, in order to supply highway and airports with oil, a supplementary highway with airfields was built down the Mackenzie Valley, and a 600-mile pipeline with its accompanying highway was built at a cost of $134,000,000. If the Mackenzie Route had been selected instead, most of this would have been unnecessary.

If the line of airports had been built down the Mackenzie Valley, the oil of Norman Wells would have been just where it was most needed—in the lower Mackenzie Valley, farthest from other sources of supply. From there it could have been distributed along the Valley by relatively cheap pipelines. In crossing the mountains to the Yukon Valley and Alaska, the pipeline could have followed low passes, instead of running counter to the general trend of the country. With the money saved, a railway could have been built, paralleling and supplementing both airline and highway. This would have been of great value in the development not only of the Mackenzie Valley, Yukon Territory, and Alaska, but also of the mineral resources of the Canadian Shield, along the western edge of which the Mackenzie System extends for more than 1,300 miles.

While it is unfortunate that this was not done when

communication with Asia was a matter of practical necessity, and the money for its cost available, it is probable that the North American sections will be built because of local needs. Whether it will ever serve its most important function—that of an interhemispherean link—will depend, like many more important matters, upon how the rival power blocs of the world resolve their differences, for it is hard to imagine the sort of society that will survive a third world war.

15

Crossroads of the World

WHEN, on December 17, 1903, Wilbur and Orville Wright made their historic flight at Kittyhawk, N. C., they started a chain of events of immense significance for the future of Canada. Before Columbus' day —and for some time afterward—the centre of the world was the Mediterranean, as its name implies. The effective peoples of the world lived along its shores:—Egypt, Persia, Greece, Rome, Portugal, Spain,—all bordered on the Mediterranean; and so long as commerce was confined to short voyages, the Mediterranean countries remained in the lead. The invention of the mariner's compass and the extension of the art of navigation brought about the discovery of the New World, and the decline of Mediterranean civilization soon set in.

It was succeeded by that in which the Atlantic peoples took the lead. Great Britain, an island on the flank of Europe, her people already trained to the sea, was well situated to benefit from this new orientation. The fortunate possession of coal and iron made it possible for her to initiate the Industrial Revolution, and to hold the centre of the stage during the greater part of the nineteenth century. By the end of that time, however, her position was being seriously challenged, especially by the United States, whose natural resources were greater than those of any other country.

The invention of the railway, which England gave to the world, made possible the phenomenal growth of the United States. In a stagecoach era, England might have continued to dominate the world; but when railways enabled the United States to exploit the possibilities of coal, iron, copper, and

171

other mineral resources in an area spread across a continent, and after petroleum was discovered, the shift beyond the Atlantic was inevitable.

The airplane has now brought about another change in the size and shape of the earth, thereby influencing the destinies of many peoples and countries, but none so much as Canada. Although they did not realize it, the Wright brothers were responsible for a new shift in the world's centre—from the Atlantic to the Arctic. To some, this statement may seem strange, even absurd, but much evidence can be produced in support of it.

Land is still vital to man's existence; and the great land masses are in the northern hemisphere, broadest toward the north. Thus the Arctic—smallest of the oceans—has the long coastline of Canada and Alaska on one side, and the even longer coastline of Eurasia on the other; between them, they practically enclose it. This was of no value in the days of ships, for the frozen ocean was an insurmountable barrier; but aircraft can navigate arctic as well as other skies; and, since the shortest routes between most points in North America and Eurasia are northward, it means that Canada's geographical position must become an increasingly important factor.

When Laurier dreamt of what Canada might do in the twentieth century, he knew nothing of aviation, nor of what it might mean; yet it may be seen that any estimate of Canada's future which fails to take account of aviation must go wide of the mark. Already the airplane has played, and is playing, an important part in opening up the North. Ordinarily, the building of aerodromes precedes the establishment of airlines; but in the North, where every lake is a landing-field, and planes can land in summer on pontoons, and in winter on skis, airlines are established ahead of airports. In the dry, clear air of the North, the absence of flying facilities considered essential elsewhere is not a great handicap, since flying-routes generally follow the major streams.

As early as 1921, charter flights were being undertaken to points northward from Edmonton by such pilots as C. H. ("Punch") Dickins, W.R. ("Wop") May, and Leigh Brintnell. In December 1926, James A. Richardson, a Winnipeg financier, organized Western Canada Airways Limited to serve outlying communities from Red Lake to The Pas; and, in 1928, Dickins on behalf of WCA inaugurated a service down the Mackenzie Valley, making the first flight to Aklavik, near the mouth of the Mackenzie, on July 1, 1929. In the latter year, the Post Office Department awarded a Mackenzie Valley mail contract to Commercial Airways. This company was absorbed the following year by Canadian Airways Limited, which in the meantime had succeeded WCA. In 1937, as already mentioned, Grant McConachie established a passenger and mail service between Edmonton and Whitehorse, with a connection to Vancouver from Fort St. John.

James Richardson had organized Canadian Airways Limited to provide air services between some of the principal Canadian cities and to continue serving northern points. He had begun to establish a fairly comprehensive service when, as part of the "economy" measures taken by the Government of Canada during the depression, his mail contracts were cancelled, and Canadian Airways was compelled to discontinue all services except those on northern routes.

This was still the situation when, on April 10, 1937, Trans-Canada Airlines was created by Act of Parliament and given a virtual monopoly of transcontinental traffic. Its first commercial flight was made between Vancouver and Seattle on September 1 of that year; and gradually, as trained staff became available and radio equipment was installed, new flights were added. By the end of 1940, regular air schedules were in operation, carrying mails, passengers, and express on the following flights: Montreal-Vancouver, Moncton-Toronto, Montreal-Toronto, Toronto-North Bay, Lethbridge-Edmonton, and Vancouver-Seattle. In that year, the total of TCA scheduled flights was over 4,500,000 miles. Since

173

then, complete services have been extended to Halifax and St. John's, and the number of daily flights on all runs has been greatly increased. On July 1, 1947, the Great Lakes Airway was opened with transcontinental flights touching at Sault Ste Marie and the Lakehead, instead of going by way of North Bay, as previously.

In the international field, Trans-Canada began regular flights between Toronto and New York in 1940; in 1943, regular flights carrying mail were begun between Canada and England, and by the end of 1945 passengers were also taken. Since then, services between Toronto and Chicago, Toronto and Cleveland, and Montreal and New York have been inaugurated, as well as to the Bahamas, Jamaica, and Trinidad.

Between 1939 and 1941, the Canadian Pacific Railway acquired 10 airlines operating in different parts of the northern regions. These included Canadian Airways, Yukon Southern Air Transport, Quebec Airways, Dominion Skyways, Wings Limited, Starratt Airways, Arrow Airways, Prairie Airways, Ginger Coote Airways, and Mackenzie Air Service; the latter, operated by Leigh Brintnell, was the principal competitor of Canadian Airways in the Mackenzie Valley. The following year the various companies were consolidated into Canada Pacific Airlines, of which Grant McConachie has since become president. In the interval, planes and other equipment have been standardized, and duplication of services has been eliminated, or services increased where required. All along the northern frontier, from Fairbanks, Alaska, to Blanc Sablon, on the Strait of Belle Isle, and Knob Lake, Labrador, CPA maintains scheduled flights.

While at first it had been intended that TCA should have a monopoly of oceanic flying, a change in this plan occurred in 1949, and the following year CPA inaugurated two Trans-Pacific services, one to Hong Kong, and the other to New Zealand and Australia, both from Vancouver. The Oriental service proceeds northwestward from Vancouver to Anchorage, in southeastern Alaska, thence to Shemya, on one of the Aleutian chain, and from there to Japan and Hong Kong. The New Zealand-Australia service is by way of San Francisco, Hawaii, and Fiji.

The air map of the northern hemisphere facing page 181 shows that although half of the world's surface is north of the equator, this area comprises three-fourths of the world's land, and nine-tenths of its population. As already mentioned, the United States is on the outward edge, along with India, China, and Egypt; while Canada, Alaska, Soviet Asia, and northern Europe form the inner circle. And since the United States, with its large population and world-wide interests lies beyond Canada, and all the main airways between the United States and most of Asia and Europe cross Canadian territory, the importance of Canada's position is evident. As settlement moves northward, providing local traffic, and as new landing-fields and increased flying aids are provided, the shorter routes will naturally attract more and more through traffic. During the second world war, when distance and time were both vital factors, Canada was indeed the Crossroads of the World. An endless stream of aircraft passed over the Northwest Staging Route to the Soviet Union; and another stream went to points in Europe by way of Gander and Goose airports.

While railway companies are sometimes inclined to look upon the airplane as a competitor, it is certain, at present at any rate, that airplane services are complementary to railways; airplanes may constitute the spearhead of the advance, but the transportation structure will doubtless continue, as in the past, to be based on railways. Since, in the first place, there could have been no Canada without railways, it may seem strange that so little railway planning has ever been undertaken by Canadian Governments. In this connection, the contrast between airplanes and railways is most striking.

No railway was ever built without governmental assistance. The Intercolonial and the Canadian Pacific were both built as national projects, one entirely by the Government, the other largely with government aid. The extension of the Grand Trunk in the early years of this century was also made possible by lavish governmental support, as was the building of the Hudson Bay Railway, which, however, has always been purely a national project, although financed mainly out of the proceeds of Prairie land sales. Yet none of these was really undertaken as part of a comprehensive scheme planned with a view to the most effective development of the country. As a matter of fact, in some cases—notably the National Transcontinental-Grand Trunk Pacific, built through a country since found to be rich in natural resources,—development was so greatly neglected that for many years the railway could be operated only at a heavy loss.

The Intercolonial was operated at a loss in the mistaken belief that it was helping to develop the country through which it passed, but the net result was that both railway and country became the victims of chronic economic stagnation. The Canadian Pacific, while originally planned to follow a course through the Rockies by way of Yellowhead Pass, making possible the settlement of a broad zone across the most fertile portion of the Prairies, kept instead to the more arid southern section; while the paralleling of the Canadian Northern and Grand Trunk Pacific, resulting in the bankruptcy of both, deferred development for a generation. The philosophy, if such it can be called, underlying all this was that railways were considered to be matters of private concern, in which Governments were only incidentally interested. This, of course, was a fallacy. Not only has no railway ever been built in Canada without substantial governmental support, but despite such support, more than half the country's railway mileage has come into Government hands through financial failure.

It should be clearly evident that railways must be built in advance of development; and that they have a most important function as developmental agencies. On the Prairies, where railway-building is comparatively cheap, and where, because land can quickly be put in crop, the railway-builder might count on traffic almost from the moment his tracks were laid, lines were often profitable from the start. But when railways began traversing territory not so easily brought under production, they ceased to be chiefly transportation agencies and took on the function of developers, a rôle for which they were not suited. Their financing did not permit of long-deferred returns; and, consequently, except for the CPR, which had large land grants and other subventions on which to rely—and less competition in its own territory—the railways, one after the other, reached the end of their resources, leaving their unofficial partners, the Governments, no alternative but to take them over. In the United States, most of the railways passed through successive reorganizations; and although many had received considerable assistance, the relationship between railways and Government was never quite so intimate as in Canada.

Because, after the first world war, the Federal Government was thus required to assume control of the greater part of Canada's railway mileage, and during the depression was faced with huge annual deficits, little additional railway building was undertaken, except where important mines, such as at Flin Flon, obviously justified short branches. This has seriously retarded the development of new areas.

In northern Alberta and British Columbia, Provincial Governments, rather than the Federal Government, have been the guarantors of railway securities, and both have had railways left on their doorstep. In the days before the first world war, when settlers were flocking into the Peace River country, J. D. McArthur, an ambitious railway promoter, began the building of two railways northward from Edmonton. One, the Edmonton, Dunvegan and British Columbia

Railway, headed northwestward to serve the Peace River country, as already described; the other, the Alberta and Great Waterways Railway, ran slightly east of north from Edmonton to Waterways, on Clearwater River, a few miles from its junction with the Athabaska, where connection was made with river steamers. Handicapped by lack of capital, these railways inched their way into their respective territories, and, to the bitter disappointment of the thousands of settlers who had anticipated their coming, reached their limited objectives years behind their originally-published schedules. Eventually, in 1920, as we have seen, the two roads were taken over by the Alberta Government and are now operated jointly by the CPR and CNR.

In British Columbia, the Pacific Great Eastern Railway, begun as a connecting-link between Vancouver and the Grand Trunk Pacific at Prince George, ceased construction before either terminus had been reached. It then languished for 30 years, most of the time unable to meet its operating expenses, and, of course, failing adequately to serve the territory through which it runs or to aid in the development of new territory, without which it could never hope to justify its existence. Recent plans for its extension and its possibilities for the future have already been discussed.

One bright spot in this picture of failure and frustration is the experience of the Ontario Northland Railway. Planned, as we have seen, as an agricultural development road, it unexpectedly helped to open up rich silver, gold, and base-metal mines, and in consequence has been able to perform its function as a transportation agency while at the same time helping to develop the country. It is significant, however, that except for those at Cobalt, the discovery of most of the other mines occurred in advance of the railway; steel did not reach Porcupine till 1911, but Dome, Hollinger, McIntyre, and other great mines at Porcupine were already in operation; similarly, the Ontario Northland's branch into Kirkland Lake and Noranda followed discovery of mines there.

Although built at such a cost of money and grief, Canada's railway network now leaves little to be desired that cannot be quite easily corrected. The CPR, by its southerly branch through the Crow's Nest Pass, and by tunnels and other betterments on its mainline, has overcome many of its earlier disadvantages. The CNR, once a group of disjointed lines, not yet fully co-ordinated when the depression struck it hard, has since been welded into a well-rounded railway. It has easy curves and grades; its roadbed and equipment are in reasonably good condition; and it operates in a region that is potentially the most productive in Canada, mostly tributary to the new zone being developed in the North. Alberta and Saskatchewan oil should make more rapid the conversion of both CPR and CNR to Diesel-electric or jet power, and this should result in lower operating costs as well as greater efficiency.

In contrast to existing mileage, what is still needed to promote the development of the North is really insignificant. Probably the two most essential new lines are the extension of the PGE to provide a Pacific outlet for the Peace River country, and the extension of the Northern Alberta Railways, or perhaps the building of a separate line, to Great Slave Lake—and eventually down the Mackenzie Valley, en route to Asia, as already described. Then, some time in the near future, a line must be built to provide more direct connection between Hudson Bay, the Mackenzie Valley, and the North Pacific. Except for branch lines, and short connections, this should provide a basic railway network, which would be adequate for some time to come. These suggested new lines through unsettled country should be built frankly as development roads, and the national interest should be recognized by the participation of the Federal Government. Furthermore, these and similar lines already being operated by the CNR might be segregated into a special publicly-owned corporation and so operated until their function as development roads is completed.

179

While the ratio between Canada's foreign and domestic trade must vary from time to time, foreign trade will always be important to Canada; and, in a country of such long distances, the cost of transportation must always be a vital factor. Therefore it is essential that goods should reach the sea by the shortest routes, and that ports should be so equipped as to attract favourable ocean services. The importance of this to Maritime ports has already been stressed, as well as the significance of the Great Lakes-St. Lawrence Waterway. Efforts should be made to take full advantage of ports in Hudson and James Bays; and as development moves northward in Ontario and Quebec, port facilities should be provided on both sides of the Bay. Churchill should, of course, be used to the fullest extent, and special studies should be made with a view to overcoming its particular problems. As already referred to in Chapter 12, full use should be made of the long-neglected port of Prince Rupert. Because of the Alaska Panhandle, which, a short distance north of Prince Rupert, cuts off the inland portion of British Columbia from the sea, that port will probably continue to be the most northerly Canadian seaport of consequence on the Pacific, and it is the logical outlet for a large section of northern British Columbia and the Peace River country.

For many years, ships, after having made the northwest or northeast passage, have gone long distances up Siberian rivers to load lumber and other products; but it was not till 1949 that a ship, after rounding the north coast of Alaska, ascended the Mackenzie River to Great Slave Lake. Now that this demonstration has been made, there is no reason why other ships should not load oil, lumber, pulpwood, fish, and mineral concentrates at points along the Mackenzie and in Great Slave Lake.

Motorists, toiling along dirt roads, or bogged down in mud,

in attempting to cross Canada by highway, might look over-
head and see luxurious planes zooming past on their way from
coast to coast, or they might be brought to a stop at some
level-crossing while a comfortable transcontinental passenger
train rolls past. For years a Trans-Canada Highway has been
talked about, but there is not yet a highway on which one
may travel from one coast to the other with any degree of
comfort. Since it was hoped eventually to link together
sections built independently by the different Provinces, without any co-ordinating agency, the project lagged hopelessly.
So serious did this situation become that the Federal Government stepped into the picture; and toward the end of 1949
Robert H. Winters, Minister of Resources and Development,
outlined a scheme under which the Federal Government
undertook to defray one-half the cost of a "modern, first-class,
hard-surfaced road, following the shortest practical east-
west route consistent with the needs of the Provinces and of
Canada as a whole."

Contracts were later entered into between the Federal
Government and a majority of the Provinces, and portions of
the ultimate route were determined upon. Naturally the
greater part of the route would be through the southern part
of the country; but in Ontario, as well as through Saskatchewan, Alberta, and British Columbia a quite suitable northern
alternative was possible. In Ontario, the only highway yet
completed is by way of North Bay, Cochrane, and Geraldton
to Port Arthur, but the route chosen follows the north shore of
Lake Superior, where a 200-mile gap still exists. In the
Rocky Mountains, the old contest between the Yellowhead
and Kicking Horse routes was again in evidence, with the
victory once more going to the latter. Conceivably the route
chosen may attract a greater number of tourists, but the more
northerly one, while also possessing fine scenery, would provide better access to territory badly needing it.

16

"A Wilful Waste . . ."

PROBABLY because of the great variety and wide distribution of their natural resources, Canadians have been careless about conservation. Lands consisting of light soils, which Nature in her wisdom had sealed over with sod, and which could have provided pasture indefinitely, have been ploughed and harrowed so as to become the sport of wind and rain; bush lands, growing thick about the watersheds of streams, which for ages have held back the run-off from the melting snow in spring, or the rain-storms of summer, have been slashed to provide stove-wood or hauled to the mill to become indifferent lumber.

The greatest loss of all is that of timber destroyed by fires caused by carelessness. The most vulnerable and at the same time most vitally important of all resources are the forests. On their preservation depends the comfort and even the safety of millions of city folk whose contact with trees consists chiefly of seeing them in public parks. Power generated by the fall of streams provides light, and sometimes heat, for homes hundreds of miles away; and the continuance of this power depends upon an unfailing water supply. Dependence of water supply upon conservation of timber has been tragically demonstrated in too many places.

To the early settler, contemplating his patch of bush-land, timber was often an unmitigated nuisance. Looking ahead, he could envisage a long vista of back-breaking days devoted to chopping down trees, wrestling with sap-sodden logs, and grubbing out stumps. Between him and the broad fields of which he dreamt, the all-pervading forest was an ever-present

182

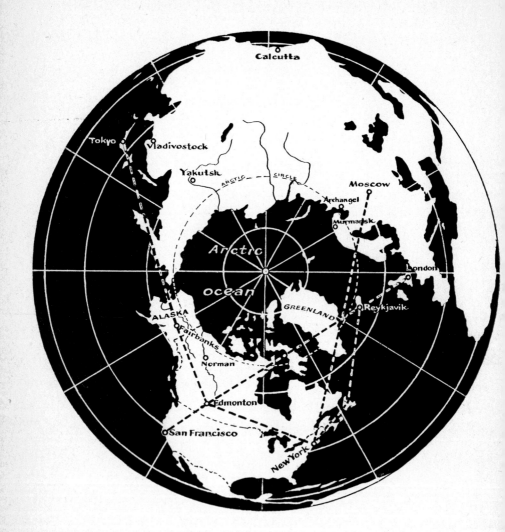

The northern hemisphere, shown above, contains three-fourths of the world's land and nine-tenths of its population. The dotted lines do not all represent actual air-routes, but mark the shortest distances between points in America and Eurasia. The route from New York to Tokyo, however, is approximately as it might now be flown and is about 3,000 miles shorter than one across the Pacific Ocean by way of San Francisco.

obstacle to be overcome; not only was it so for him, but also for those who were prevented by it from becoming his neighbours. The advantage of a ready supply of fuel, logs for buildings, and rails for fences was far outweighed by the depressing effect of the forest, covering everything like a blanket, darkening the face of the land, and making travel extremely difficult.

Before the lumbermen arrived, the spear-shaped region that is almost surrounded by the Great Lakes, now called Old Ontario, was practically unbroken forest, consisting, along the shores of Lakes Ontario and Erie, of mixed hard and soft woods; and along the shores of Lake Huron and Georgian Bay, of a greater proportion of white pine and red pine. Much of the land to the eastward, as far as the Ottawa Valley and northwestward of there, was also covered with pine, which, farther into the Precambrian Shield, changed to spruce, balsam, and jack pine. The white and red pine, in addition to being most accessible, was in greatest demand, and it attracted loggers whose market for saw-logs was the United States, where the timberlands of the middle-western States had only recently been denuded of their more accessible timber.

The disappearance of the forests of Old Ontario was a great national loss; yet in many sections the land covered by them was much too valuable to justify its being kept indefinitely for tree-culture. Much more serious is the fact that larger regions of rougher land, suited to the growing of trees, have been denuded of their timber by preventable fires. If the great loss every year through fire and pests, but especially fire, could be saved, a great step would be taken in the conservation of forest resources; and if, in addition, such provision were made that every area cut over was regenerated either naturally or by the planting of seedlings, the forests could supply in perpetuity greater quantities of better timber than they do now.

Undoubtedly, the greatest single step that could be taken is the control of forest fires. In this connection, every person who enters the woods, from the casual camper to the timber-contractor, and every agency, private or governmental, concerned with the forest resources has a responsibility to help reduce the present disgraceful national loss through preventable forest fires.

According to the latest available figures (1948), over 39 per cent of all timber cut is used for lumber; 33 per cent for pulp and paper; 24 per cent for domestic fuel; and four per cent for miscellaneous purposes. It is likely that in the near future the latter group will show the greatest increase, since it includes a growing number of products—at the expense of which of the others the increase will be is yet too soon to say. Scientists believe that the Age of Wood is only about to begin, and the number and variety of products derived from wood are increasing very fast.

Canada's lumber industry comprises about 7,500 active sawmills of all sizes and description, but there are only 123 pulp and paper plants,—32 making pulp only, 64 making both pulp and paper or paper boards, and 27 making only paper boards. Ninety-eight of the above are in the Provinces of Ontario and Quebec, leaving only 25 for the rest of Canada. Some of these plants are enormous, such as that of Pacific Mills Limited, at Ocean Falls, B. C., of the Spruce Falls Company, at Kapuskasing, and of the Abitibi Company, at Iroquois Falls, both in Ontario, and the Bowater plant, at Corner Brook, Newfoundland. Pulp and paper now constitutes the country's greatest manufacturing industry, with a gross production in 1949 of $836,148,393.

Although paper from rags had been made in Canada since 1803, it was not till 1866 that wood became the raw material of paper. At first, the industry grew slowly; but as the timber resources of the northwestern States became depleted, and especially after 1913, when the customs duty on newsprint was abolished in the United States, the Canadian newsprint industry really began to get into its stride. In 1913, the production of newsprint in Canada amounted to only 350,000 tons, which had increased to 2,725,000 by 1929 when, due to over-production and falling off of demand, most of the mills found themselves in financial straits. Since then, with the cessation for some years of new plant construction, the industry has got back on its feet. In 1949, production of newsprint amounted to 5,176,327 tons.

According to official figures, Canadian forests comprise a total of 1,274,840 square miles, but of this area only 701,232 square miles is considered capable of effective production, that is to say, of steadily producing timber suitable for commercial and domestic needs; and of this much smaller area, only about 437,000 square miles is considered economically accessible at the present time. Furthermore, only about 42 per cent of the productive area bears trees large enough for saw-logs, pulpwood, or fuel, while the balance consists of young growth of various ages, species, and uses.

Estimates from the same source give the rate of depletion of reserves of merchantable timber during the years 1939-48 at 34,162,384,000 cubic feet, of which 79 per cent was devoted to commercial and domestic use, while the remaining 21 per cent comprised losses by fire and pests, fire averaging 40 per cent, and insects and fungi 60 per cent. Furthermore this depletion is mostly concentrated in the 473,000 square miles of accessible forest referred to above, which means that replacement of normal depletion in this area alone would require an average growth of 11.28 cubic feet per acre per year. Although the average annual growth is not known, it is commonly assumed to be about 14 cubic feet.

It must be noted that this figure of 14 cubic feet is given as the average increment for all Canada, varying from a low of perhaps five cubic feet per acre in some northern areas to about 80 cubic feet per acre in parts of British Columbia and southern Ontario. The rate of depletion, either from cutting or from fire or pests, does not always coincide with the rate of growth for that particular area; in fact, in some places the highest rate of depletion is found where the regeneration rate is, if not the lowest, at least extremely low.

Conflict has developed, especially in some parts of Ontario, between sawmill men and those engaged in the pulp and paper industry, whose interests clash, quite often to the detriment of the forests. Major General Howard Kennedy, appointed as a Royal Commissioner, reported at length in 1947 on this and other aspects of forest conservation in Ontario, and his report emphasizes the difficulty of reconciling the interests of those whose (wood) crops require a century to mature with those who can make use of their timber in little more than half that time. This is especially significant when it is realized that the present market value of the first mentioned is much less than that of the second.

In general, the Provinces are responsible for the forests, but the Federal Government is also greatly concerned with their perpetuation. This has been recognized by Parliament which, in 1949, passed the Canada Forest Act, providing for Federal participation in the conservation and development of forest resources.

The conservation and adequate use of Canada's coal measures is another subject that transcends provincial boundaries. On the basis of estimated coal reserves, Canada is one of the greatest coal countries in the world, but, so far, most of this coal has played a very small part in the national economy; the two principal industrial provinces are close to United States coalfields and consequently derive most of their coal from such sources. Aside from deposits in Nova Scotia, and lesser ones in New Brunswick and Vancouver Island, Canada's principal coal areas are in or adjacent to the Rocky Mountains region. As we have seen, immense deposits of bituminous coal exist in the Prairie regions of Alberta, shading into lignite in Saskatchewan and anthracite in the foothills of the Rockies. Semi-anthracite and low-volatile bituminous coal also exist in the Peace River and Ground-hog areas of British Columbia.

The oilfields of Alberta, which extend into Saskatchewan and northeastern British Columbia, offer a cheaper and more easily-transported fuel which cannot fail to have an adverse effect upon the coal industry, not only in that region, but even in Nova Scotia and on Vancouver Island. It would appear that the present practice of digging coal out of the ground and hauling it to the point of use is no longer efficient, and some other method of utilizing its power should be devised. For this and other reasons, it seems advisable that there should be some agency, national in scope, whose duty it would be to work out a long-range program for the more effective utilization of Canada's coal resources. Later in this chapter the establishment of a Conservation Commission is suggested, and this might very well be one of its functions.

Just as the supply of timber is sometimes assumed to be inexhaustible, so has the soil been considered as something that will last forever, without much effort being made to preserve or regenerate it; yet, all over the country, especially in sections that have been settled the longest, lands which once supported many people are being abandoned as incapable of supporting anyone. In some places, soil improperly put to use is actually lost through the action of frost, wind, or water, causing the depopulation of some areas and creating favourable spots for the propagation of weeds. Forest fires not only destroy trees, but quite often the soil as well. Soil depletion reduces production, thus leaving less revenue for schools, roads, and other improvements, and results in a lower scale of living, with far-reaching consequences.

Those on newer land, where this process has not yet become evident, sometimes assume that their land is inherently different from that in older communities, and fail to take advantage of the lessons to be learned. Later, when the penalty of neglect overtakes them, it is too late for individual action.

In 1949, the Ontario Legislature appointed a Select Committee on Conservation which made a study of soil depletion, flood control, reforestation, and allied subjects. Its report, made in 1950, discloses a serious situation and contains a number of recommendations which, if acted upon, might help to correct some of the worst evils. While the Committee's attentions were directed mainly to the more southerly sections of the province, where the problems are much greater, conditions in some of the northern districts were also dealt with. Concerning timber conservation in the southern portion of the Precambrian Shield (mainly between Georgian Bay and the Ottawa River), the Committee recommended the reforestation of 3,600 square miles within the next 25 years.

In dealing with settlement in the Clay Belt, the Committee pointed out the need for large-scale drainage, clearing and breaking of the land, but also pointed out that to do this effectively heavy machinery is required, which is beyond the means of individual settlers. The report further points out that "the transition from forestry to agriculture can be relatively quick, but it will require at least 60 years to return an area to a forest economy once it has been cleared for agricultural settlement."

One other recommendation is significant:

> The opening of any settlement area in the northern clay belts must initially be on the basis of a combined husbandry of field and forest. This combined economy should gradually give way to one of primary agriculture in which forests continue to give balance to land use. Recognizing the value of forests within an agricultural community, and its contribution to an overall economy, provision should be made when opening new townships or areas for settlement to set aside a percentage of the area for community forests.

One of the most serious situations disclosed by the survey was the effect which the removal of forest cover is having

on the water supply in many parts of Ontario. It was found
that the supply of some two million persons was endangered
by the destruction of timber which had formerly held back
the melting snow in spring, and also prevented the immediate run-off of rain water, thus lowering the underground level
over large areas of Old Ontario.

Soil and water are as vital to human life as air itself; that
neither is inexhaustible is being painfully demonstrated in
many parts of Canada. Underground water is not a factor in
northern Canada—that is to say, in the Precambrian region,
—but the influence of timber cover upon the supply of surface water might be taken into consideration in arriving at a
comprehensive forest program for Canada.

As soil, water, and air seem inexhaustible to many, so also
do minerals within the rocks; yet a pound of iron, or copper,
or zinc, once removed, can never be replaced. Nevertheless,
it is futile to caution people against using such metals as they
may reasonably require for fear that some day, perhaps a
thousand years hence, a generation may find that the end of
them has come. Furthermore, since most of the minerals
now being mined have been discovered through surface
showings, it is but reasonable to assume that for every out-
crop there are thousands of other deposits beneath the surface that might be discovered by the scientific methods now
being more generally used, and which might indefinitely
postpone the inevitable day when the mineral resources will
become exhausted.

Not only that, but all metal put to use need not necessarily
be charged to the debit side of the national stock-sheets.
Properly used, it is of much more value to humanity than
lying dormant in the ground; and after it has served its term
of usefulness as machinery or equipment it can often be
returned to the smelter and again converted into the raw
material of industry. A very large proportion of the iron,

copper, lead, and other metal that comes from the smelters goes into the furnaces as scrap.

We have seen, in the experiences of Cariboo and Klondike, how flitting is the life of a placer camp. Lode-mining, at least so far in Canada, is not quite so precarious, yet in many places there are townsites that were built around some mine which eventually reached the end of its ore and closed down, forcing all dependent upon it to pull up stakes.

Such an experience is at present facing the people of Sherridon and Cold Lake, in northern Manitoba, where the Sherritt Gordon mine, in operation over 20 years, will shortly shut down. Fortunately for most of those concerned in this case, the Sherritt Gordon Company has an alternative undertaking. It controls the copper-nickel deposits at Lynn Lake, already mentioned, to which the mine plant and most of the houses in the old townsites are being moved. Although the indications are that the Lynn Lake operations will be much more permanent than those at Sherridon, the moving of an entire community of several thousand people entails not only a great deal of inconvenience, but a great deal of expense as well. While it is true that most of the benefit from the operations at Sherritt Gordon has accrued to those who directly participated, nevertheless production of the mine over the past two decades has been of value to Canada as a whole, and it should be possible to spread the cost of this transfer over a larger section of the community.

In his address as president of Section IV of the Royal Society of Canada (Geological Sciences Including Mineralogy), in May, 1940, Dr. J. J. O'Neill, Dean of Engineering at McGill University, advocated the establishment of a board whose function, among others, would be the formulation of long-range plans covering contingencies such as this one. "Long before our mines wane by depletion," he said, "the large and growing population of our new mining districts, and all the services which are now absolutely dependent on the mines and their communities, should be assured a permanent, if somewhat different, place in our national development."

Dr. O'Neill cited the Porcupine area, which may also be used here for purposes of illustration. In and around Timmins live about 40,000 people dependent upon the output of its gold mines. There is no intention to suggest that any of these is about to reach the end of its effective life, but that day must come for all of them. Probably, by that time, Porcupine will have many more people, and many additional millions will have been invested in business and residential property. If it is inevitable that all this should depend entirely upon the productiveness of gold mines—to say nothing of the vagaries of the international monetary situation—with no suggestion of an alternative, then, of course, such a thing must be accepted as a natural risk by those who follow mining as a way of life, but this need not necessarily be the case.

On the other hand, Porcupine is adjacent to a good agricultural area where livestock of all kinds can be raised, and large yields of dairy produce, poultry, eggs, honey, and field crops of all sorts can be produced. Hydroelectric power generated by rivers flowing to James Bay is now used by the mines and could be transferred, if not so required, to industrial purposes. The Hudson Bay Lowland region, within 150 miles of Porcupine, contains large deposits of lignite hitherto of little value, which could possibly be converted into fertilizer. The same region is underlain by deposits of high-grade gypsum from which a wide variety of building products could be manufactured. It also contains beds of excellent fire and china clay which could become the basis of an important ceramics industry. Furthermore, within 50 miles of Porcupine are large deposits of asbestos which could supply raw material for other industries.

A board similar to that suggested by Dr. O'Neill once existed, and during its life performed valuable services. It might be revived. Appointed by the Laurier Government in 1909, it was called the Commission of Conservation, and consisted of representatives of the Federal and Provincial Governments, with 20 additional members chosen for their special qualifications. Its functions were advisory and consultative. From time to time it made recommendations concerning the better use and conservation of natural resources. It collected information, making it available to the Governments concerned and to the general public.

One of its first undertakings was a national survey of water-power; and for many year its reports were the principal source of information on the subject. Productivity and conservation of the soil was another matter upon which the Commission made studies and reports; and it seems probable that had it not been abolished in 1921 many of the conditions now so deplored might not have become quite so serious.

In the interval, a change has occurred in public thinking on such matters. It is now more generally recognized that Governments must have bodies of experts on whom they can rely. The National Research Council, established in 1916, and since greatly extended in scope, is one of these. In a general way, its function is the encouragement of scientific research in all fields. It has charge of important investigations on behalf of the Government, and acts as an advisory and consultative agency for various departments, acting also in a similar capacity for industry. In the light of experience resulting from the valuable services performed by the National Research Council, it is perhaps safe to say that were such a body as the Commission of Conservation in existence today, it would find a wide field for its efforts.

Although beyond the field of conservation, there is another function which such a body might perform. In various ways the division of the country into provinces with their more or less arbitrary allocation of jurisdictions, often tends to discourage activity on a nationwide scale and to encourage sectionalism. Some of the effects of this have already been pointed out, and the need for some sort of joint planning agency seems obvious. No business could operate successfully that did not have a pretty clear idea of its objectives and the steps necessary to attain them; and a nation, too, must have some idea of where it is going and of how it proposes to get there. Parliament is, of course, the final authority; but with the multiplicity of matters with which Governments are now faced, members have not the time, even if they had the qualifications, to plan the details of long-term programs, often of a highly technical nature. Aside from the practical value of such a board, it would, of course, have the advantage of being required to think in terms of Canada, rather than of any one section.

17

Land of Destiny

IN the preceding pages, the reader has been conducted on a tour of the most potentially productive parts of Canada. I think I have succeeded in showing that the country can produce in abundance practically everything needed to provide a high scale of living for a very much larger number of people than it now possesses; and that the output of mines, forests, farms, and fisheries will probably always leave surpluses for sale abroad. Among the essentials, only cotton, citrus fruits, tea and coffee—and to a lesser extent, tobacco, —cannot be produced, while wool production is not yet equal to the demand.

As Canada pushes her frontier farther north, developing her resources and adding to her people, she should as a matter of right take her place among the great nations of the earth. Already she is playing a much greater part in world affairs than her size and intrinsic national importance might seem to justify. This is partly due to the reflected glory of association in the British partnership and because she is a close neighbour of the United States; but it is also because she so obviously has no selfish interests to serve, and therefore excites neither the suspicion nor the fear of any country.

As she grows in size and potential strength, however, and her interests spread throughout the world, some of this trust will doubtless be sacrificed. Consequently, in order to retain the confidence of others, Canadians will need to have, among other things, a lively appreciation of their own responsibilities as the custodians of such a large share of the world's bounty. One way in which they can make it clear that they do recog-

nize this responsibility would be to offer a haven to many
more refugees from less fortunate countries. Canadians cor-
dially invite the investment of capital, irrespective of whence
it comes, so why should they not more generally extend a
welcoming hand to those who show a desire to make their
home in Canada?

Canada has thus a splendid opportunity to make a virtue
of necessity, since her most obvious lack at present is people.
In every Province that reaches into the North this need is
very great, not only for settlers to occupy the land and produce food for workers in the new industries and developments, but also to serve as workers themselves, without whom
there can be no new industries and very little new development. That during the winter of 1949-50 there were over
300,000 unemployed persons in Canada is less an indication
that opportunities cannot be provided for more people than
that adequate steps were not taken to make existing opportunities available to a greater number.

In most cases, the days of small-scale operations are gone.
The projects discussed in the preceding pages all require
large aggregations of capital. Even in the agricultural field,
traditionally a one-man show, the man with little more than
his own muscle will not by such means do much to develop
the vacant lands of the zone that now awaits development.
Settlement of that region must be undertaken on the basis of
well-planned, large-scale projects by which lands are cleared
and drained, roads are built, and electric power made available over considerable areas at a time. The cost of this should
be assessed against the land and paid off over periods of
sufficient length to permit of its being done without seriously
jeopardizing the occupants' scale of living.

In the past, during times of unrestricted immigration,
people were encouraged to flock into the country, irrespective
of whether their chances of success were good or not; railways were built at the whim of promoters, townsites were
laid out, and new territory was opened up without much

thought as to whether the people so attracted would be provided with the minimum requirements of decent living. The result has been that of the millions who eagerly passed through Canadian ports, almost as many have departed. It is possible that many of those who left would have done so in any event: the United States may have been their destination from the first; but it is also possible that if human life had not been held so cheap, and a more concerted effort been made to encourage them to remain, many of the millions who merely stopped off in passing might have stayed to become Canadians. As it was, in many places, settlers hopefully took up homesteads, only, after a period of frustration, to move on; communities, enthusiastically started, saw their enthusiasm dwindle and die after all who could get away had done so.

Canadians were misled by the great success achieved by the United States, when millions of people from every country in Europe besieged her shores, quickly spread from ocean to ocean, built great cities, established vast industries, and within a generation or two created the world's outstanding country. Many thought that as soon as vacant lands in the United States were filled, history would repeat itself north of the border; but they overlooked the immense cost in human lives, the wasted effort and money, by which that result had been attained. They also failed to realize that conditions of life in Canada are not quite the same, and that methods which succeeded in the United States, even at such a cost, might not be successful in a different country. They were not aware that with the close of the pioneering era in the United States, that type of settlement, peculiar to North America, had practically ceased forever. Insofar as the Prairie regions of Canada were concerned, where land requires no clearing, and wheat can be grown with a minimum of care and attention, settlement was possible, even though the returns quite often scarcely justified the effort. On the other hand, in the parkland beyond the prairie to the north, where land must be cleared, settlement was not as general, with the result that marketing facilities were not provided to the same extent as in the Prairie region.

Consequently, if Canada is to fulfil the destiny that seems possible for her, she will need many millions of new people, —people to settle the vacant spaces along the northern frontier; to help build the cities that must come into being; and to work in the mines, power plants, pulp mills, and factories so that the wherewithal of a continuing civilization may be provided at all times. Because a few who arrived in the early years of the century found it difficult to adjust to the Canadian scene, some people are still prejudiced against immigrants from many parts of the world; but I need only refer such sceptics to the rolls of western colleges for a refutation of the charge that any considerable groups have failed to make good. Not only are the grandchildren of immigrants enrolled in disproportionate numbers, but their parents constitute a large part of the warp and woof of western society. There is no reason to suppose that those who might come to Canada in these times are any less likely to make good, especially if advantage be taken of the many lessons to be learned from the past, and if future immigrants are not expected to put up with the harshness and carelessness to which many of their predecessors were subjected.

And what of Canada's own Lost Legion? What about the millions of Canadian-born who, year after year, have crossed into the United States to the enrichment of that land, never to return to their own? That this has been allowed to continue for so long was perhaps inevitable in a country whose people so generally have had the limited view of its possibilities already described. A country that considered itself a long, narrow strip bordering the northern boundary of the United States, and hemmed in by a vast inhospitable region to the north, could not have been expected to provide a very high scale of living for its people, and naturally the more progressive ones looked elsewhere for opportunities denied them at home. It is therefore idle to speculate on what might have happened had these emigrants remained, since it is doubtful if they could have done a great deal to influence the prevailing attitude. On the other hand, since Canada has not been able to retain all her sons and daughters, it is fortunate that they should have had, so near at hand, such a congenial foster home.

It will be seen that this book has steered clear of any discussion concerning the type of economic measures that may be necessary in order for Canada to achieve her destiny. It is assumed that Canadians will be able to meet any situation that may arise without being so paralyzed by fear of change that they can do nothing, or stampeded into change without a fairly clear idea of where they are going. If there is a country in the world in which the present economic system may survive, for a time at least, it is Canada; she still has an abundance of natural wealth from which many more people than she is likely to have for a very long time can extract a relatively good living. If this should not prove possible, the fault will probably lie with economic conditions elsewhere, most likely in the United States. Notwithstanding this, if what is called free enterprise is to survive, modifications will doubtless be necessary, in future as in the past, to meet changing conditions; but if such modification should not prove adequate, the history of Canada suggests that Canadians are competent to cope with whatever situation might arise.

In the early years of the second world war, much consideration was given to problems thought likely to become urgent after the war, when millions of armed personnel and workers in wartime factories and other temporary agencies would need to be re-established in the community. And it is probably due to this early and continuous planning that so orderly a transition from war to peace was possible, which a comparison with conditions after the first world war will amply confirm. In 1941, a Committee on Reconstruction, headed by Principal Cyril James of McGill University, was appointed by the Government of Canada to study many aspects of this problem. In its various reports the Committee insisted that full employment must be a first-requirement of post-war economy, and suggested that, in order to ensure this, production would need to be kept at a high level. It was not possible at that time to foresee what the post-war economic picture would be, but it was correctly assumed that many countries would be faced with a need for goods far greater than their ability to pay in a currency acceptable to the sellers. Dr. James therefore recommended that: "If Canada is going to sell goods abroad either it must take payment in goods or services produced in other countries, or it must frankly express its willingness to supply such goods as a long term capital investment to be paid either by principal and interest in traditional fashion or to be repaid intangibly by better relations and a better ordered world."

This high note has not always been sustained; but, if Canada, with so much of the world's natural wealth within her borders is to justify her possession of it, and at the same time continue to keep her people fully employed (at the scale of living indicated by the Committee), it may be necessary to make many more of the good-will investments to which Dr. James referred.

During the war, nothing was too difficult, or even too quixotic, for the Canadian people to undertake; they frequently faced what seemed to be the impossible, only to discover that the impossible did not exist so long as there was a determination to overcome any and all obstacles. Perhaps it was too much to expect that the wartime pace could continue indefinitely, but with respect to mining and oil development, at least, an exception can be made. While Shipshaw cost a great deal more than would have been necessary under normal conditions (a feature which need not be repeated), the vision and energy with which that project was undertaken and carried through are still very much to be desired, and, as a matter of fact, are in evidence at many places along the northern frontier. If this should eventually bring about a well-rounded development of the North, that in itself should provide reason to hope that Canada might sometime attain the place in the world to which her fortunate geographical position and her resources would seem to entitle her.

This book has attempted to show that Canada possesses the material requirements of greatness:—minerals unequalled in quantity and variety; power, consisting of hydroelectric energy, coal, petroleum and natural gas; timber for lumber, pulp, and the products of wood-chemistry; ample food; splendid waterways and harbours; and an unexcelled geographical position. Nevertheless, these, essential though they may be, do not necessarily add up to national greatness. The human element must also be considered, and the question may fairly be asked: do the Canadian people possess the qualities needed for the creation of a great nation?

Perhaps it might be well at this point to consider what sort of people Canadians are. Is there now a distinct Canadian type, and how is it distinguished? The Canadian people are generally considered to comprise two principal strains, one loosely termed Anglo-Saxon, the other French; and these are becoming more and more intermixed with one another and with a number of other strains of European origin.

It must be admitted that, despite the length of time that the ancestors of many Canadians have been in Canada, an appropriate way of life has not yet been evolved; Canadians wear clothing designed for the climates of other lands, usually too hot in summer and too cold in winter; their houses are not well suited to their needs chiefly because they are planned by architects whose art is largely imported from more temperate regions, producing houses that fail to meet the requirements of the Canadian climate. Since houses without some sort of central heating could scarcely be lived in, that un-European novelty has been supplied; but ventilation and air-conditioning, which, both for comfort and health, are made necessary by central-heating, are largely neglected. Such a situation is probably inevitable in a sparsely-settled country whose ways are derived from other lands and have not yet been adapted to the new setting. With a larger population, and as greater national consciousness develops, it is possible that Canadian customs will more closely conform to the conditions imposed by climatic and other considerations.

One of the commonest criticisms levelled at Canadians is that they are disunited. Is this true? Divided as they have been in the past by geographical barriers, actual and imaginary, it would be strange if they did not sometimes fall into sectionalism; and yet it is remarkable how similar, comparing one part of Canada with another, their reactions often are. As is perhaps natural in certain special circumstances—such, for example, as the conscription issue in Quebec, or economic matters on the Prairies,—they may at times seem to take a sectional view; but when it comes to questions concerning Canada as a whole, whether in the newest Province of Newfoundland, the Maritimes, Quebec or Ontario, the Prairies, or British Columbia, they think very generally along similar lines. Usually, they can be counted on to support anything they are persuaded is for the welfare of their country.

To that extent, at least, it can be said that there has emerged from this group of once-separate colonies, with diverse local interests, an individual known as a *Canadian*, even though he may still resemble a Highland Scot in Cape Breton or a Breton in Gaspé. Sometimes he may be persuaded to think as a Quebecker, or a Maritimer, or an Ontarian, or a Westerner rather than as a Canadian; but these are merely momentary lapses, and it seems evident that those who occasionally succeed in deluding him into such thinking rarely retain his confidence for very long. Therefore, it can be said that Canadians have one of the intangible qualities necessary for greatness: the ability to act together for the common good.

So, we come back to the question with which this book opened: will the twentieth century eventually prove to have been Canada's? It is impossible to foretell what the Canadian people will do in the years to come, but it seems safe to say that no people have a better chance to build a truly great nation. Opinions may differ as to what constitutes greatness; and while it will probably be admitted that no country which fails to provide a reasonably high standard of living for all its people can, in this democratic age, lay much claim to greatness, it may be argued that this is not the only criterion. It is still possible that the high level of material well-being which Canada can provide may nevertheless fall short of creating the culture-bed of a great people; for true greatness consists of much more than the mass-production of those mechanical contrivances which contribute so largely to the comfort and convenience of life. Ireland is a poor country, with none of Canada's vast stores of natural wealth, yet it has produced an unusually large proportion of persons who have greatly influenced their times, not only in their own homeland, but throughout the world.

It will thus be seen that greatness is an elusive and somewhat variable quality, and that it comprises many factors which in combination determine the place and influence of a people among the nations of the world. However, the manner in which Canadian statesmen are accepting much more than their share of responsibility in world affairs; the energy and determination with which Canadians, in some places, are going about the development of their natural resources; and the eminence attained in the arts and sciences by a growing number of Canadian men and women may be cited as signs of an emerging greatness which might tend to encourage the hope that in due course it may truly be said that the twentieth century was indeed Canada's.

Bibliography

Albright, W. D.: "Crop Growth in High Latitudes," *Geographical Review*, October, 1933.
"Gardens of the Mackenzie," *Geographical Review*, January, 1933.

Alcock, F. J.: "Geology of Lake Athabaska Region," *Geological Survey of Canada*, Memoir no. 196, 1936.

Antevs, Ernst: *The Last Glaciation, with Special Reference to the Ice Retreat in Northeastern North America*, (American Geographical Society, Research Series no. 17). New York, 1928.

Ball, M. W.: "Development of the Athabaska Oil Sands," *"Transactions of the Canadian Institute of Mining and Metallurgy*, vol. 64, 1941.

Bell, James Mackintosh: "Great Slave Lake," *Geographical Review*, October, 1929.
Economic Resources of Moose River Basin, (Report of the Bureau of Mines, 1904). Toronto, 1904.

Bethune, W. C.: *Canada's Eastern Arctic: Its History, Resources, Population, and Administration*, Ottawa, 1935.
Canada's Western Northland: Its History, Resources, Population, and Administration, Ottawa, 1937.

Blanchet, G. H.: *Keewatin and Northwestern Mackenzie: A General Survey of the Life, Activities, and Natural Resources of this Section of the Northwest Territories*, Ottawa, 1930.

Bostock, H. S.: "Potential Mineral Resources of Yukon Territory," *Geological Survey of Canada*, Paper 50-14, 1950.
Physiography of the Canadian Cordillera, With Special Reference to the Area North of the Fifty-Fifth Parallel, Geological Survey of Canada, Memoir no. 247, 1948.

Burpee, Lawrence J.: *The Search for the Western Sea*, Toronto, 1908.

Campbell, Marjorie Wilkins: *The Saskatchewan* (Rivers of America Series), New York, 1950.

Camsell, Charles and Malcolm, W.: "The Mackenzie River Basin", *Geological Survey of Canada*, Memoir no. 108, pp. 99-104, 1921.

Canada's Century

Cockfield, W. E. and Bell, A. H.: "Whitehorse District, Yukon," *Geological Survey of Canada*, Paper 44-14, 1944.

Cole, Arthur A.: "Ontario's Route to the Sea", *Canadian Geographical Journal*, vol. V, no. 3, 1932.

Coleman, A. P.: "Northeastern Part of Labrador, and New Quebec," *Geological Survey of Canada*, Memoir no. 124, 1921.

Davies, Raymond Arthur: *Arctic Eldorado*, Toronto, 1944.

Dawson, C. A. and Murchie, R. W.: *The Settlement of the Peace River Country. A Study of a Pioneer Area.* (Canadian Frontiers of Settlement, edited by W. A. Mackintosh and W. L. G. Joerg, vol. VI), Toronto, 1934.

Dawson, C. A. (ed): *The New North-West*, Toronto, 1947.

Dawson, George M.: *Report on an Expedition in the Yukon District, N. W. T. and Adjacent Northern Portion of British Columbia, 1887, with Extracts Relating to the Yukon District from a Report on an Exploration in the Yukon and Mackenzie Basins, 1887-88 by R. G. McConnell*, Ottawa, 1898.

Deacon, William Arthur: *My Vision of Canada*, Toronto, 1933.

Desbarats, G. H.: "Surveying on the Hamilton River, Labrador," *Canadian Geographical Journal*, November, 1948.

Finnie, Richard: *Canada Moves North*, Toronto, 1942.

Flaherty, R. J.: "The Belcher Islands of Hudson Bay: Their Discovery and Exploration," *Geological Review*, June, 1918.

Freeman, H. E. and McGuire, B. J.: "How the Saguenay River Serves Canada," *Canadian Geographical Journal*, November, 1947.
    "Wealth From the Canadian Shield," *Canadian Geographical Journal*, May, 1949.

Futcher, Winnifred M.: *The Great North Road to Cariboo*, Vancouver, 1938.

Harrington, Lyn: "The Welland Canal," *Canadian Geographical Journal*, May, 1947.
    "North on the Hudson Bay Railway," *Canadian Geographical Journal*, August, 1947.

Harrington, Richard: "Coppermine Patrol," *Canadian Geographical Journal*, December, 1950.

Hooke, A. J.: "Alberta, Nature's Treasure House," *Canadian Geographical Journal*, October, 1950.

204

Bibliography

Hubbard, Mina B.: *A Woman's Way Through Unknown Labrador,* London, 1908.

Hume, G. S. and Link, T. A.: *Canol Geological Investigations in the Mackenzie River Area, Northwest Territories and Yukon,* Ottawa, 1945.

Hutchison, Bruce: *The Fraser* (Rivers of America Series), New York, 1950.

Innis, Harold A.: "The Hudson Bay Railway," *Geographical Review,* January, 1930.

    Settlement and the Mining Frontier, (Canadian Frontiers of Settlement, Edited by W. A. Mackintosh and W. J. G. Joerg, vol. IX), Toronto, 1936.

Jenness, Diamond: *The People of the Twilight,* New York, 1928.

Jolliffe, A. W.: "Mineral Possibilities of N.W.T.," *Canadian Mining and Metallurgical Bulletin,* November, 1937.

Keenleyside, Hugh L.: "The Forests of Canada," *Canadian Geographical Journal,* July 1950.

Kidd, D. F.: "Great Bear Lake—Coppermine River Area, Mackenzie District, Northwest Territories," *Geological Survey of Canada,* Summary Report, 1931, pt. C, 1932.

Kindle, E. M.: *Canada North of Fifty-Six Degrees: The Land of Long Summer Days,* Ottawa, 1928.

Kitto, F. H.: *Athabaska to the Bay, Report of a Reconnaissance Expedition, Chiefly by Canoe, from Edmonton and McMurray across the Northern Parts of Alberta, Saskatchewan, and Manitoba, to Port Nelson and Churchill on Hudson Bay, 1918,* Ottawa, 1919.

    The Peace River District, Canada: Its Resources and Opportunities, Ottawa, 1920. Revised edition: *The Peace River Country,* Canada, Ottawa, 1928.

Lanks, Herbert C.: *Highway to Alaska,* New York, 1946.

LeBourdais, D. M.: *Northward: On the New Frontier,* Ottawa, 1931.

Leechman, Douglas: *Eskimo Summer,* Toronto, 1946.

    "Yukon Territory," *Canadian Geographical Journal,* June, 1950.

    "First Men in the New World," *Canadian Geographical Journal,* November 1949.

Link, T. A.: "The Western Canada Sedimentary Basin Area," *Canadian Mining and Metallurgical Bulletin,* July 1950.

Lloyd, Trevor: "The Mackenzie Waterway: A Northern Supply Route," *Geographical Review,* July, 1943.

Lord, C. S.: "Mineral Industry of the Northwest Territories," *Geological Survey of Canada,* Memoir 230, 1941.

Low, A. P.: "Report on Explorations in the Labrador Peninsula Along the East Main, Koksoak, Hamilton, Manicuagan and Portions of Other Rivers in 1892-93-94-95." *Geological Survey of Canada,* Annual Report, vol. VIII, 1895.

MacKay, Douglas: *The Honourable Company; a History of the Hudson's Bay Company,* Indianapolis, 1936.

MacKay, R. A. (ed): *Newfoundland, Economic, Diplomatic, and Strategic Studies,* Toronto, 1946.

Mackenzie, Alexander: *Voyages from Montreal through the Continent of North America to the Frozen and Pacific Oceans in 1789 and 1793, etc.* London, 1801; Toronto, 1902.

Neilson, James M.: "The Mistassini Territory of Northern Quebec," *Canadian Geographical Journal,* October, 1948.

Ogilvie, William: *Early Days on the Yukon,* New York, 1913.

O'Neill, J. J.: *The Geology of the Arctic Coast of Canada, West of the Kent Peninsula.* Report, The Canadian Arctic Expedition, 1913-1918, vol. 11.

Pike, Warburton: *The Barren Grounds of Northern Canada,* London, 1891.

Porsild, A. E.: *Reindeer Grazing in Northwest Canada: Report of an Investigation of Pastoral Possibilities in the area from the Alaska-Yukon Boundary to the Coppermine River,* Ottawa, 1929.

Rasmussen, Knud: *Across Arctic America: Narrative of the Fifth Thule Expedition.* New York and London, 1927.

Report of the Royal Commission Appointed by Order-in-Council of Date May 20, 1919, to Investigate the Possibilities of the Reindeer and Musk-Ox Industries in the Arctic and Sub-Arctic Regions of Canada, Ottawa, 1922.

Roberts, Leslie: *The Mackenzie,* (Rivers of America Series), New York, 1949.

Bibliography

Robinson, J. Lewis: "Canada's Western Arctic," *Canadian Geographical Journal*, December, 1948.

Seton, Ernest Thompson: *The Arctic Prairies: A Canoe-Journey of 2000 Miles in Search of the Caribou, Being an Account of a Voyage to the Region North of Aylmer Lake.* New Edition, New York, 1943.

Skelton, Oscar D.: *The Railway Builders*, Toronto, 1916.

Stead, R. J. C.: "The Yellowhead Pass," *Canadian Geographical Journal*, August, 1948.

Stefansson, V.: *The Friendly Arctic*, New York, 1921; New edition, 1943.

My Life With the Eskimo, New York, 1913.
Hunters of the Great North, New York, 1922.
The Northward Course of Empire, New York, 1922.

Stefansson V. and Wiegert, Hans. W.: (eds) *Compass of the World*, New York, 1943.

Stefansson V., Wiegert Hans W. and Harrison, R. E. (eds): *New Compass of the World*, New York, 1949.

Stephens, G. W.: *The St. Lawrence Waterway Project*, Montreal, 1929.

Stewart, Elihu: *Down the Mackenzie and Up the Yukon in 1906*, London, 1913.

Tanner, V.: *Outlines of the Geography, Life and Customs of Newfoundland-Labrador*, (2 vols), Cambridge, 1947.

Taylor, Griffith: *Canada*, London, 1947.

Thomson, Lesslie R.: "St. Lawrence Problem, Some Canadian Economic Aspects," *The Engineering Journal*, April, 1929.

Tyrrell, James W.: *Across the Sub-Arctics of Canada*, Toronto 1897.

Tyrrell, J. B.: "Report on the Country Between Athabaska Lake and Churchill River," *Geological Survey of Canada*, Annual Report, vol. VIII, 1896.

Vancouver, George: *Voyage of Discovery to the North Pacific Ocean*, London, 1798.

Williams, M. Y.: "Churchill, Manitoba," *Canadian Geographical Journal*, September, 1949.

Williamson, O. T. C.: *The Northland: Ontario*, Toronto, 1946.

Wilson, J. A.: "The Expansion of Aviation into Arctic and Sub-Arctic Canada," *Canadian Geographical Journal*, September, 1950.

Index

Canada's Century

Caribou, 155, 157
Carrot River, 79
Chibougamau, 36
Chicoutimi, Que., 40
Chinook Winds, 127
Churchill, Man., 6, 71, 82, 83, 84, 88, 91, 92, 181
Churchill River, 68-69, 70, 74
Civilization based on minerals, 3
Clearwater River, 69, 70, 178
Coady, Dr. Michael, 29
Coal Deposits
  Alberta Plains, 107, 189; Groundhog Basin, 187; New Brunswick, 24, 186; Nova Scotia, 19, 24, 186; Peace River, 187; Rocky Mountain Foothills, 186; Vancouver Island, 186; Yukon, 151
Cobalt, Ont., 53, 54, 178
Cochrane, Ont., 54, 56, 59, 181
Columbia Cellulose Company, 140
Columbia River, 125, 134
Commission of Conservation, 191
Commission on Reconstruction, 199
Connell, F. M., 150
Consolidated Mining and Smelting Company of Canada Limited, 76, 127
Corbett, Dr. A. E., 29-30
Corner Brook, Nfd., 28
Cornwall, J. K. 97, 98
Creighton, Tom, 72

Dawson, Y. T., 148, 166
Dawson Creek, B. C., 108, 114, 131
Delano, Warren, 168
Department of Transport, 166
Dingman, A. W., 96
Dome mine, 54, 179
Dominion Steel and Coal Corp., 19
Douglas, James, 129
Dubawnt River, 153
Dunvegan, Alta., 111

Eaton Canyon (New Quebec), 23
Edmonton, Alta., 75, 82, 95, 99, 103, 104, 108, 113, 116, 118, 166
Eldorado mine, 78, 115
English River, 70
Ellesmere Island, 154
Eskimos, 160-161
Exploits River, 27

Fairbanks, Alaska, 99, 166, 175
Fenimore Iron Mines Limited, 22
Finlay River, 111
First Americans, 162-163
Fitzgerald, Alta., 76
Flin Flon, Man., 69, 72, 73, 178
Fond du Lac River, 74
Forests
  British Columbia, 132, 137, 140; New Brunswick, 28; Nova Scotia, 29; Ontario, 59, 183, 186; Quebec, 34; statistics, 184-186
Fort Chimo Mines Limited, 22
Fort Nelson, B. C., 166
Fort St. John, B. C., 111, 112, 166
Fort Smith, N.W.T., 76, 151
Fort William, Ont., 64-65
Franklin, District of, 11, 147, 153
Fraser River, 125, 127, 131-132, 134
Frobisher Limited, 22, 75

Gander Airport, 16, 176
Gaspé Peninsula, 12, 28, 30
Gatineau River, 44
Geological Survey of Canada, 52, 100
Geraldton, Ont., 63, 64, 182
Giant Yellowknife mine, 75
Glace Bay, N. S., 19
Globe & Mail (Toronto), 57
God's Lake, 90
Goldfields, Sask., 74
Goose Airport, 16, 176
Gouin Dam, 37
Government
  Alberta, 113, 178, 179; Borden, 85; King, 47, 87; Ontario, 10, 52; Quebec, 20, 37, 47; Union, 47, 87
Grande Prairie, Alta., 113, 166
Great Bear Lake, 53, 67, 78, 107, 151, 152
"Great Circle" waterway, 142
Great Lakes—St. Lawrence Waterway, 11, 45-51, 92, 180
Greatness, What constitutes? 204
Great Slave Lake, 75, 76, 77, 78, 100, 107, 115, 118, 151, 152, 153, 163, 180
Grimshaw, Alta., 76
Gulf Oil Company, 103

Haileybury, Ont., 52, 58, 63
Halibut, 140, 141

Index

212

Index

Thelon River, 153
The Pas, Man., 73, 79, 83, 85, 90, 91, 174
Thomson, Dr. Lesslie, 49
Timiskaming Lake, 43, 52, 53
Timmins, Noah, 55
Timmins, Ont., 56, 191
Titanium, 26
Tomkins, Dr. James, 29
Toronto, Ont., 2, 87, 118
Trans-Canada Highway, 92, 180-181
Tyrrell, Dr. J. B., 153
Tyrrell, J. W., 153

Ungava Peninsula, 23, 147
United Keno Hill Mines Ltd., 150
United States, 8, 103
Uranium, 74, 78, 115, 151

Val d'Or, Que., 35-36
Vancouver, B. C., 118, 137-138, 166, 179
Vancouver Island, 127, 136
Vanderhoof, B. C., 133
Ventures Limited, 22, 73, 76

Vermilion, Alta., 112, 118, 119
Victoria, B. C., 127
Victoria Island, 154

Washington, Treaty of, 51
Waterways, Alta., 76
Watson Lake, Y. T., 166
Welland Canal, 50, 51
Wells, B. C., 129
Whitehorse, Y. T., 99, 148, 151
Willims Creek, 127, 128
Winnipeg Lake, 8, 67, 71, 80
Winnipeg, Man., 68, 70, 79, 81, 82
Winnipeg River, 70
Winters, Hon. R. H., 181
Wright-Hargreaves mine, 57
Wright, W. H., 57

Yale, B. C., 129, 130
Yellowhead Pass, 130, 131, 132, 177, 182
Yellowknife, N.W.T., 75, 77, 78, 117, 151
Yukon River, 8, 148, 149
Yukon Territory, 11, 124, 147

Arctic Ocean
Melville Id.
Devon
Banks Id
Victoria Id
Alaska
Aklavik
Coppermine
Dawson
YUKON
Ft. Norman
NORTH-WEST
GREAT BEAR L.
Whitehorse
TERRITORIES
Yellowknife
GREAT SLAVE L.
Chesterfield Inlet
Peace R.
Vermilion
ATHABASKA
Churchill
Peace River
BRITISH
Prince Rupert
Prince George
ALBERTA
Edmonton
MT. ROBSON
COLUMBIA
SASKATCHEWAN
Flin Flon
The Pas
Saskatoon
Calgary
Victoria
Vancouver
Regina
Winnipeg
Seattle
Missouri R.
Pacific Ocean
UNITED